Dr. Robert Wolff's Great Body, Great Life Program

A week-by-week planner to recharge your body and change your life

Robert Wolff, Ph.D.

Adams Media Corporation
Avon, Massachusetts

Published by Adams Media Corporation
57 Littlefield Street, Avon, MA 02322. U.S.A.
www.adamsmedia.com

ISBN: 1-58062-761-7

Printed in Canada.

J I H G F E D C B A

This book is available at quantity discounts for bulk purchases.
For information, call 1-800-872-5627.

INTRODUCTION

Inside each of us is a voice calling us to change. The voice and its message never cease: the desire to make changes in body, heart, and soul. Yet, in the quest to heed the call, we can be stopped dead in our tracks by the daunting task of absorbing so much information from so many sources. This is especially true for health, fitness, and nutrition. Who and what are we to believe?

Dr. Robert Wolff's Great Body, Great Life Program is a book written to give you what you need to change your body and motivate and inspire you at the same time. You're going to find quick tips for exercise, nutrition, and motivation every week, giving you a complete year's guide for simple, easy changes you'll see and feel beginning the first week.

One of the biggest causes holding people back from changing how they look and feel is the belief that exercise, eating right, and keeping oneself motivated takes too long or is too difficult and demanding. Not true.

Dr. Robert Wolff's Great Body, Great Life Program helps eliminate such belief as its tips are brief, powerful, positive, unique, and among some of the most effective you'll find at bringing about significant change in a very brief amount of time. Every tip—a total of 208—found inside the book is chosen to be easily usable in your lifestyle, regardless of the time you have or your experience level.

HOW TO USE THIS BOOK

In addition to the book's weekly tips, you'll also find a weekly guide that will allow you to chart your progress from the changes you'll see and feel—both the physical to the emotional.

At the end of each great week for you, take a moment and write down a review of your progress on the success you've made. As you fill in the spaces provided from week to week, you will be amazed at how the little things you do add up to big changes. This process of recording your simple steps will be an extremely powerful motivator for you that will keep you on track should you ever get sidetracked, think you're not progressing fast enough, or have those feelings of wanting to quit.

The power of such reinforcement—of seeing and feeling first-hand how your life and body are changing each week—will be highly motivating. You'll experience this power anytime you turn the pages back to the previous weeks and read the notes you made about the changes you see and feel taking place in your body and life and realize how quickly and how far you've come.

Dr. Robert Wolff's Great Body, Great Life Program is the daily and weekly guide that will give you what you desire: a fast and simple way to change how you look and feel in only minutes each week.

MANY THANKS TO . . .

Claire Gerus and everyone at Adams Media for the fine work they do. And to you, my reader friend. May this book inspire you to make the changes you want and show you how to do it simply, easily, and faster than you may have ever imagined possible. Be blessed.

DISCLAIMER

Before starting any new exercise or nutritional program, be sure to talk to your doctor. If you have any serious medical conditions or if you are taking medication, get your physician's consent before you begin.

1 WEEK

"Where the mind goes, the body follows."

—Anonymous

One disciplined action will bring you many rewards. To prove this, let's say you've taken the action to eat healthier foods. Just by that one action . . .

- Your body now has more energy because of the healthy foods you are eating.
- You feel better and are not so sluggish.
- Your digestion has improved.
- You sleep better.
- Your complexion has improved.
- You're saving money because, on average, it costs you less to eat healthy foods than processed and junk foods.
- You're getting leaner each week—losing the fat and keeping your lean muscle tissue—because you're now eating foods containing the proper ratio of protein, carbohydrates, and fat.
- You're feeling and looking better, and your appearance is improving, thereby raising your self-confidence, self-image, and self-esteem.

All these things help improve your relationships with others, increase your job performance, and raise your belief that you can set goals and achieve them. And because you see and feel the results of just one disciplined action of eating more nutritiously, you now have a strong desire to begin an exercise program that will change your body and the way you feel even more quickly—not to mention, give you more rewards!

THIS WEEK'S EXERCISE TIP

To tighten glutes and legs while walking and without exercise equipment, try lengthening the stride of your walk. To make it more aerobic, really swing those arms up and down, forward and backward. By taking longer steps, you activate more glute, quad, and hamstring (back leg) muscles, and as you know, a well-worked muscle quickly becomes a well-toned and good-looking muscle.

THIS WEEK'S NUTRITION TIP

When buying tuna in spring water, always check the label. Fat content—even from the same company and the same brand—can vary quite substantially. The reason? Tuna caught closer to the shore are leaner (less fattier foods in their diets) than tuna caught farther out to sea (more abundant sea life and higher fat diets). Don't believe me? Just go to the store and see for yourself.

THE LITTLE THINGS I DID THIS WEEK

FOR NUTRITION:

....

....

....

....

....

....

....

....

....

FOR EXERCISE:

....

....

....

....

....

....

....

....

THE LITTLE THINGS I DID THIS WEEK

TO CHANGE MY THINKING:

TO HELP INSPIRE MYSELF:

THE LITTLE THINGS I DID THIS WEEK

THE CHANGES I CAN SEE:

THE CHANGES I CAN FEEL:

WEEK 2

"*Every year I live I am more convinced that the waste of life lies in the love we have not given, the powers we have not used, the selfish prudence that will risk nothing, and which, shirking pain, misses happiness as well. No one ever yet was the poorer in the long run for having once in a lifetime 'let out all the length of the reins.'*"

—MARY CHOLMONDELEY

THIS WEEK'S MENTAL TIP

One of the easiest ways to change how you feel is through the power of affirmations. Simply tell yourself what you want to experience (for example, in weight loss, you'd say something like "I look and feel great at ____ pounds") and keep repeating it at various times through-out the day; early morning and late evening are best. Affirmations activate the unconscious section of the mind—the real powerhouse that changes your life—by giving it new commands on which to act. The key to making affirmations work is that they must be positive and always stated in the present tense; as if you've already achieved that change in your life right now.

THIS WEEK'S EXERCISE TIP

Drink plenty of water before doing any exercise. Some research has shown that for every 1 percent of weight your body loses from dehy-dration (i.e. loss of water), your peak performance can drop by 10 percent.

THIS WEEK'S NUTRITION TIP

For a more restful sleep, try eating some carbohydrates about ninety minutes before bedtime. The reason? Carbs help boost serotonin lev-els in the body, and serotonin helps the body relax and is one of the three neurotransmitters commonly known as "the feel-good hor-mones." Just don't eat too many. Like any nutrient, too many carbs, especially before bedtime, can make you gain weight.

THE LITTLE THINGS I DID THIS WEEK

FOR NUTRITION:

....

....

....

....

....

....

....

....

....

FOR EXERCISE:

....

....

....

....

....

....

....

....

THE LITTLE THINGS I DID THIS WEEK

TO CHANGE MY THINKING:

....
....
....
....
....
....
....
....
....
....

TO HELP INSPIRE MYSELF:

....
....
....
....
....
....
....
....
....

2

THE LITTLE THINGS I DID THIS WEEK

THE CHANGES I CAN SEE:

....

....

....

....

....

....

....

....

....

THE CHANGES I CAN FEEL:

....

....

....

....

....

....

....

....

3
WEEK

"There is only one thing that will really train the human mind and that is the voluntary use of the mind by the man himself. You may aid him, you may guide him, you may suggest to him, and, above all else, you may inspire him. But the only thing worth having is that which he gets by his own exertions, and what he gets is in direct proportion to what he puts into it."

—ALBERT L. LOWELL

THIS WEEK'S MENTAL TIP

To keep progressing when others have stopped, always change your program. Never do the same thing twice. This will help spike your metabolism and help keep your body off-guard, never quite giving it the chance to habituate and get stale. Not to mention, it keeps you motivated and looking forward to your next workout because you're always doing something new and different.

THIS WEEK'S EXERCISE TIP

For incredible looking calves, the best exercise is done without weights or equipment or in a gym. It's your stairs! Without shoes on, simply place the balls of your feet (the top one-third of your foot) on the edge of the stairs. Keeping your knees locked, allow your heels to lower below the stair; then raise your heels up above the stairs as high as you can. Do this movement nonstop until you begin feeling a burning sensation in your calves. Stop for fifteen to twenty-five seconds and then do it again two more times. After you've finished all three sets, lower your heels all the way down and stretch your calves by staying in this position for thirty to fifty seconds. Expect to be sore the next day or so. Repeat the exercise only when you can no longer feel any soreness. In thirty days you'll be amazed at the changes.

THIS WEEK'S NUTRITION TIP

To lose weight, try this simple but very effective European secret that spas and retreats have used for years. Chew your food twenty times before swallowing. Twenty times, that's all, and you'll be amazed at how something so simple could be so effective. Not only will your food take longer to eat—which will give your brain a more accurate and quicker message from the stomach that you're getting full—but properly chewed food is actually digested more easily and its nutrients are used more effectively by the body.

THE LITTLE THINGS I DID THIS WEEK

FOR NUTRITION:

....

....

....

....

....

....

....

....

....

FOR EXERCISE:

....

....

....

....

....

....

....

....

THE LITTLE THINGS I DID THIS WEEK

TO CHANGE MY THINKING:

....

....

....

....

....

....

....

....

....

....

TO HELP INSPIRE MYSELF:

....

....

....

....

....

....

....

....

....

THE LITTLE THINGS I DID THIS WEEK

THE CHANGES I CAN SEE:

....

....

....

....

....

....

....

....

....

....

....

THE CHANGES I CAN FEEL:

....

....

....

....

....

....

....

....

....

3

4
WEEK

"Be content with what you have; never with what you are."

—B. C. FORBES

THIS WEEK'S MENTAL TIP

Stay sensitive to feedback. While exercising, keep your mind focused on your body and listen to what it tells you during and after each exercise. Are your muscles in tune with and feeling the movement? Does it feel like you're in the groove and moving like a well-tuned machine? Or, is your body telling you to change things because it's not feeling what you're doing? Even in the middle of a set or exercise, don't be afraid to stop and try something else. Find the thing that your body wants you to do for it that day, that hour, and that minute! Your body is a living, dynamic organism that's constantly changing throughout the day, and it's always talking to you. Keep your mind focused on it, and you'll hear it loud and clear.

THIS WEEK'S EXERCISE TIP

Looking for a great aerobic and anaerobic workout but short on time? Easy. Do more in less time; that's the secret for fitness success. During your workout, simply decrease your rest time between exercises and sets to no more than thirty-five seconds. The combination of exercise and less rest time increases heart rate, amps metabolism, gets blood pumping throughout your body, and floods your body with those wonderful natural opiates (the "feel-good hormones") called endorphins.

THIS WEEK'S NUTRITION TIP

To make skim milk taste more like regular milk, put it in the freezer for fifteen minutes before drinking. The colder the milk the richer it tastes. And speaking of skim milk, if you want to increase your daily protein intake, which helps increase firm muscle tone, try adding fortified skim-milk powder to yogurt, cottage cheese, soups, and desserts. Not only is it a terrific nonfat protein source, but you'll get all the benefits of the extra power-packed protein your body needs and you won't even taste the difference.

THE LITTLE THINGS I DID THIS WEEK

FOR NUTRITION:

FOR EXERCISE:

THE LITTLE THINGS I DID THIS WEEK

TO CHANGE MY THINKING:

....
....
....
....
....
....
....
....
....
....
....

TO HELP INSPIRE MYSELF:

....
....
....
....
....
....
....
....
....

4

THE LITTLE THINGS I DID THIS WEEK

THE CHANGES I CAN SEE:

....

....

....

....

....

....

....

....

....

....

THE CHANGES I CAN FEEL:

....

....

....

....

....

....

....

....

4

5
WEEK

"Did you ever hear of a man who had striven all his life faithfully and singly toward an object, and in no measure obtained it? If a man constantly aspires, is he not elevated?"

—HENRY DAVID THOREAU

THIS WEEK'S MENTAL TIP

One of the most powerful techniques to change your body and your life is through visualization. But, if you really want fast results, add the power of *feelization*. Like the name implies, feelization is when you actually feel—through your imagination—what it would be like to be ten pounds lighter or have flatter abs or tighter glutes and thighs. In essence, imagining how your body will feel—a preview—before you actually reach that goal helps propel your unconscious mind that much faster to the fulfillment of your desired result.

THIS WEEK'S EXERCISE TIP

To tone the waist and side abdominal area, do trunk twists with a broom handle. Place and hold the wooden handle on your shoulders with it resting on the base of your neck. Either seated or standing, twist from side to side nonstop for two to five minutes. To avoid a thick waistline, stay away from weights. Many people who have used weights for side abdominal work report easy muscle gains that have thickened their waistline but extreme difficulty in trying to lose that muscle while trying to get leaner. Unless you want a more-or-less permanent addition of muscle and a bigger waistline, stick with the broomstick.

THIS WEEK'S NUTRITION TIP

Think only nutrition affects cholesterol in your body? Think again. Here's a simple trick to raise the good cholesterol (HDL) in your body. Do at least ten minutes of aerobic activity like walking, biking, or any other exercise that gets your heart and lungs pumping.

THE LITTLE THINGS I DID THIS WEEK

FOR NUTRITION:

FOR EXERCISE:

THE LITTLE THINGS I DID THIS WEEK

TO CHANGE MY THINKING:

TO HELP INSPIRE MYSELF:

5

THE LITTLE THINGS I DID THIS WEEK

THE CHANGES I CAN SEE:

....

....

....

....

....

....

....

....

....

THE CHANGES I CAN FEEL:

....

....

....

....

....

....

....

....

5

WEEK 6

"We can accomplish anything we feel the urge to do. We all have within us the capacity to achieve what our souls desire. It all depends on the extent of our will power, and our ability to sacrifice unimportant things for the all-important goal. This alone is the measure of our achievement. No obstacles are too great. No matter what our past mistakes may have been, no matter how the false years may have misled and neglected us, it is never too late to start anew, never too late to attain to that complete expression of the self which alone makes for richly contented living."

—STANWOOD COBB

THIS WEEK'S MENTAL TIP

Always remember the mental principle of The Last Deposit. This principle states that your mind always remembers most strongly the last experience of anything you do. That's why when it comes to your workouts or exercise, always make sure you end your training/exercise session by doing something positive, like that extra rep, extra effort, or anything else that leaves you feeling good about yourself. It'll be the first thing you remember when it comes time for your next exercise session.

THIS WEEK'S EXERCISE TIP

To elevate your metabolism and speed fat burning, try jumping rope. In fact, you don't even need a rope. Simply place your feet together, begin moving your arms like you are swinging a jump rope and start jumping up and down. And you don't need to jump high; an inch or so works great. Just keep the momentum going by jumping up and down twenty to thirty times. Rest twenty to thirty-five seconds and do another twenty to thirty. Rest twenty to thirty-five seconds and do one more set of twenty to thirty jumps. After your third set, check your pulse rate and you'll feel it beating faster, you'll be sweating a little (maybe even a lot) and feeling great. For best fat-burning results, do it for at least fifteen minutes before breakfast.

THIS WEEK'S NUTRITION TIP

After a workout, drink a can of diluted fruit juice. Try mixing half a can of seltzer or carbonated water with half a can of fruit juice. Not only will you reduce your calories by 50 percent, but it will help your body better absorb the carbohydrates in the fruit juice to replenish the muscle fuel (glycogen) it used during your workout—and it tastes great!

THE LITTLE THINGS I DID THIS WEEK

FOR NUTRITION:

....
....
....
....
....
....
....
....
....
....
....

FOR EXERCISE:

....
....
....
....
....
....
....
....
....
....

THE LITTLE THINGS I DID THIS WEEK

TO CHANGE MY THINKING:

....

....

....

....

....

....

....

....

....

....

TO HELP INSPIRE MYSELF:

....

....

....

....

....

....

....

....

....

6

THE LITTLE THINGS I DID THIS WEEK

THE CHANGES I CAN SEE:

....

....

....

....

....

....

....

....

....

....

THE CHANGES I CAN FEEL:

....

....

....

....

....

....

....

....

....

6

7
WEEK

"As soon as you trust yourself, you will know how to live."

—Johann Wolfgang von Goethe

THIS WEEK'S MENTAL TIP

Use the power of momentum. The hardest thing for many people is just getting started, especially when it comes to exercise and eating better. One of the laws of physics states that an object will stay at rest until it's acted upon by an outside force. I say, "A body will stay out of shape and lethargic until it's set into action by an inside force." That means changing those self-limiting thoughts and beliefs and taking action. Just do a little something each day in the direction of making your body stronger and healthier. Just one little action, that's all. This sets in motion the power of momentum and momentum is awesomely powerful. If you were to place a couple of two-by-fours under the wheels of a sixty-ton locomotive, you'd keep it from moving. But, once you remove those blocks and let that train start moving and gaining momentum, it can crash through a wall of concrete ten feet thick! That's the power of momentum. Use it and you'll change your body and life.

THIS WEEK'S EXERCISE TIP

Want an easy way to work and change the appearance of those outer and inner legs? When doing the next set of leg exercises or any other leg exercise, simply change your foot position and feel the difference. To work more outer thigh, keep feet close together and pointing straight in front of you. For inner thigh, turn feet outward. For both positions, always be sure your knees travel in a straight line over your big toes.

THIS WEEK'S NUTRITION TIP

For better digestion, have a piece of papaya before your meals. Papaya contains an enzyme called papain that helps break down the proteins you eat and helps your body better use nutrients. For many people, a slice of tomato or pineapple works well, too.

THE LITTLE THINGS I DID THIS WEEK

FOR NUTRITION:

....

....

....

....

....

....

....

....

....

7

FOR EXERCISE:

....

....

....

....

....

....

....

....

THE LITTLE THINGS I DID THIS WEEK

TO CHANGE MY THINKING:

TO HELP INSPIRE MYSELF:

7

THE LITTLE THINGS I DID THIS WEEK

THE CHANGES I CAN SEE:

....

....

....

....

....

....

....

....

....

....

7

THE CHANGES I CAN FEEL:

....

....

....

....

....

....

....

....

....

WEEK

"*People who are unable to motivate themselves must be content with mediocrity, no matter how impressive their other talents.*"

—ANDREW CARNEGIE

THIS WEEK'S MENTAL TIP

With patience and persistence, you can achieve anything. But to be persistent, you've got to be motivated, and that can be a tough thing to do. Here's a little trick that will help you stay motivated to change how you look and feel. Each day for twenty days on a little Post-It note, write down one reason why you want to look and feel different and tape it to a sheet of paper. Look at yesterday's and all the previous reasons first thing in the morning and last thing at night before bed. At the end of twenty-one days, you will feel some huge changes inside. Whenever you feel a bit less motivated, simply look at all the reasons you wrote down and that'll put you back on the right road.

THIS WEEK'S EXERCISE TIP

Looking for a great facelift, you need only do once a week that will keep your face and neck looking young and vibrant without surgery? You've found it and it's called "the jaw extension." Simply keep your neck up and head erect. With the biggest smile you can make, tense your neck at the same time. Now, hold both in that position for ten seconds then release for only one to two seconds and do it again for another ten seconds. Repeat until you've done it six times. Do this only once per week and watch what happens.

THIS WEEK'S NUTRITION TIP

When it comes to nutrition, one size doesn't fit all, but here's a tip that seems to work very well for lots of people. Many have found that simply by adjusting the time of day they eat carbohydrates greatly affects their body weight. The key, it seems, is to eat most of your high carbohydrate foods early in the day (morning through 1:00 to 2:00 P.M.); then taper them down, and from early afternoon through the evening, do just the opposite and make most of the foods you eat protein.

THE LITTLE THINGS I DID THIS WEEK

FOR NUTRITION:

....

....

....

....

....

....

....

....

....

....

FOR EXERCISE:

....

....

....

....

....

....

....

....

8

THE LITTLE THINGS I DID THIS WEEK

TO CHANGE MY THINKING:

....

....

....

....

....

....

....

....

....

....

....

TO HELP INSPIRE MYSELF:

....

....

....

....

....

....

....

....

8

THE LITTLE THINGS I DID THIS WEEK

THE CHANGES I CAN SEE:

....

....

....

....

....

....

....

....

THE CHANGES I CAN FEEL:

....

....

....

....

....

....

....

....

8

WEEK 9

"*Nothing in life is to be feared; it is only to be understood.*"

—MARIE CURIE

THIS WEEK'S MENTAL TIP

Fear is one the biggest reasons why people don't ever achieve what they dream of or say they want. Has fear kept you from looking and feeling your best? If the fear of not knowing how you'd feel with a better looking body or the fear of not knowing what to do to get it or the fear of what if you aren't successful on "this diet" or "this work-out" has kept you from taking any action, it's time to let go of them today. You'd be absolutely amazed at just how many people who look and feel great today had the same, and many times, worse fears than you. We all have had fears of one kind or another in our lives. And it's when you let go of them and let go of the way it's been, that you then begin, at that moment, to experience the way it can be.

THIS WEEK'S EXERCISE TIP

Here's a great way to turn your driving time (e.g., sitting at a stoplight) into a mini-workout, one that will do fabulous things for your chest, shoulders, and arms. To work your chest, while keeping your arms straight out in front of you, place the inside of your wrists against the outside of the steering wheel in the ten o'clock and two o'clock positions. Don't grip the wheel. Now try squeezing the steering wheel and hold that squeeze for six to ten seconds. Release and repeat two more times. For shoulders, simply do the opposite; place the outside of the wrists on the inside of the steering wheel and push out (opposite of squeezing); hold for six to ten seconds. For arms, place both palms of your hands under the steering wheel and tense the biceps. Hold this position for six to ten seconds.

THIS WEEK'S NUTRITION TIP

Many people—especially women—are deficient in iron. They feel tired and rundown and wonder why. One of the best sources of iron, along with other B vitamins, is molasses. Molasses is made from the residue left after making sugar out of sugar cane, and just a little of the stuff can do wonders for your energy and health. Add a little dark molasses to muffins, waffles, and whole grain breads. One tablespoon of molasses (depending on the kind) can provide up to 75 percent of the daily iron allowance.

THE LITTLE THINGS I DID THIS WEEK

FOR NUTRITION:

....

....

....

....

....

....

....

....

....

FOR EXERCISE:

....

....

....

....

....

....

....

....

9

THE LITTLE THINGS I DID THIS WEEK

TO CHANGE MY THINKING:

....

....

....

....

....

....

....

....

....

TO HELP INSPIRE MYSELF:

....

....

....

....

....

....

....

....

....

9

THE LITTLE THINGS I DID THIS WEEK

THE CHANGES I CAN SEE:

THE CHANGES I CAN FEEL:

10
WEEK

"Men are all alike in their promises. It is only in their deeds that they differ."

— Jean-Baptiste Molière

THIS WEEK'S MENTAL TIP

Perhaps one of the biggest ways you lose power in achieving your dream—be it changing your body or anything else—is to tell others what you plan to do. Many years ago, I found that internal momentum creates external action and the more momentum I created on the inside, the faster my plans on the outside would become reality. Then I discovered why that worked. Think of all the things you want to accomplish as being like a big pressure cooker. For that cooker to work as it's designed to, it must build up enough steam power. It's the same way for you. If you tell too many people too early what you're planning to do, your internal pressure cooker loses steam and it seems to take forever, if ever at all, to reach your dream. However, if you have enough steam, as in letting the excitement build inside you and keeping your secret silent, it fires your engine to want to achieve your goal more quickly and with more focus and determination.

THIS WEEK'S EXERCISE TIP

Traveling and staying in a hotel no longer has to be bad for your body if you know some of the tricks to working out on the road. Here's a great one for legs, butt, calves, and heart. Forget the elevator and find the stairs. Part one is the stride, which works front and back legs and butt. Just like lunges or step aerobics, take one leg at a time and step up to next higher step and then back down. Then do the other leg; step up and then down. Repeat nonstop fifteen to twenty times. If one step is easy, then go for two or three steps at a time. Now here's where things get good. Part two of the stair workout will work inner and outer thighs and butt. Instead of going up the stairs forward like you did in part one, you'll be doing it sideways. Go for only one step at a time since your lateral (sideways) motion will not be as flexible as your forward and backward movement. Be sure to work both legs equally for equal results.

THIS WEEK'S NUTRITION TIP

Here's a great all-natural stress and tension reliever that's ages old, yet very few know about. Mix one teaspoon of sage leaves (known as nature's sleep helper), one tablespoon of rosemary leaves (known as nature's tranquilizer), and each ounce of dry peppermint leaves (known as nature's digestive). Mix everything and keep in an airtight container. Boil water and use one heaping teaspoon of the mixture to one cup of boiling water. Allow the mixture to steep for about one minute in the cup of hot water and the strain into a fresh new cup. Add honey to sweeten and drink with small sips. Talk about relaxing mind and body au natural!

THE LITTLE THINGS I DID THIS WEEK

FOR NUTRITION:

FOR EXERCISE:

10

THE LITTLE THINGS I DID THIS WEEK

TO CHANGE MY THINKING:

....

....

....

....

....

....

....

....

....

TO HELP INSPIRE MYSELF:

....

....

....

....

....

....

....

....

10

THE LITTLE THINGS I DID THIS WEEK

THE CHANGES I CAN SEE:

THE CHANGES I CAN FEEL:

10

53

11
WEEK

"He who is silent is forgotten; he who abstains is taken at his word; he who does not advance falls back; he who stops is overwhelmed, distanced, crushed; he who ceases to grow greater becomes smaller; he who leaves off, gives up; the stationary condition is the beginning of the end."

—HENRI F. AMIEL

THIS WEEK'S MENTAL TIP

There's a rather unspoken law of nature that says either you're growing or you're dying; there's no in-between. Nature will not deviate from her ways for anyone or anything, and it's the same for your body, mind, and spirit. Inside of you is a very powerful desire to learn and experience new things and grow in all areas of your life. Listen to your heart's desire for change and growth, act on it, and you find a sense of deep fulfillment and happiness. Refuse to hear and follow its call, and you feel unfulfilled. Each day, do just one little action to make your body look and feel better and nature will reward you bountifully.

THIS WEEK'S EXERCISE TIP

Who said you can't have a great quick body tone-up at work or school? I'm about to give you a great one for your lower stomach. Simply sit on the edge of your chair or desk. Keep your upper body erect and knees close together. Lift the knees up just a few inches and really feel it work your lower stomach area. Only a few inches is all you need. Slowly lower the legs a few inches and repeat. Do this as many times as you can; then rest twenty to thirty-five seconds and repeat two more times.

THIS WEEK'S NUTRITION TIP

Looking for a great midmorning/afternoon pick-me-up snack but don't want to spend a lot of money? Look no farther than the bagel. In tests against many of those convenient, but high-priced, energy bars, which one do you think was better for athletes looking for energy? Did you say bagel? That's right, for much less than 50 percent of the cost of that bar, you can have a nutritious bagel (pick your favorite kind) that many have found gives them more energy and lasts longer.

THE LITTLE THINGS I DID THIS WEEK

FOR NUTRITION:

....

....

....

....

....

....

....

....

....

FOR EXERCISE:

....

....

....

....

....

....

....

....

11

THE LITTLE THINGS I DID THIS WEEK

TO CHANGE MY THINKING:

....
....
....
....
....
....
....
....
....
....
....

TO HELP INSPIRE MYSELF:

....
....
....
....
....
....
....
....
....

11

THE LITTLE THINGS I DID THIS WEEK

THE CHANGES I CAN SEE:

....

....

....

....

....

....

....

....

....

....

THE CHANGES I CAN FEEL:

....

....

....

....

....

....

....

....

11

12
WEEK

"We have more ability than will power, and it is often an excuse to ourselves that we imagine that things are impossible."

—François de La Rochefoucauld

THIS WEEK'S MENTAL TIP

How you look and feel has nothing to do with how you *can* look and feel. Your life and experiences thus far have nothing to do with all the *possibilities* that are available and waiting for you to experience. Today, I want you to do one little exercise or nutrition tip you don't usually do. It could be something as easy as drinking an extra glass of water or using fat-free salad dressing or maybe it's trunk twisting twenty times from side to side or squatting up and down ten times. Whatever it is, just do something different today and you will have broken through the familiar comfort zone (translation: The Rut) and put yourself on the road to terrific results.

THIS WEEK'S EXERCISE TIP

It's time to throw in the towel. Wrap a bath towel around both door handles of any door in your home to do a great exercise for your back. Place the door so that you're looking at the inside of it (the thinnest part of the door where the dead bolt sticks out). Grab each end of the towel and wrap the middle of the towel around both of the handles. While holding both ends of the towel, step back until the towel is taut. With a slight bend to your legs and your body upright, lean back away from the door. Now with only your arms, pull your body close to the door and then allow it to lean back again. Do this nonstop eight to twelve times and then rest for twenty to thirty-five seconds and repeat two more times. This is a great exercise that will tone both arms and back.

THIS WEEK'S NUTRITION TIP

How about some energy that will stay with you for hours and is actually good for you? Try adding beans to your diet. They are rich in complex carbohydrates and will also help reduce LDL (the bad cholesterol) in your body.

THE LITTLE THINGS I DID THIS WEEK

FOR NUTRITION:

....

....

....

....

....

....

....

....

FOR EXERCISE:

....

....

....

....

....

....

....

12

THE LITTLE THINGS I DID THIS WEEK

TO CHANGE MY THINKING:

....

....

....

....

....

....

....

....

....

....

....

TO HELP INSPIRE MYSELF:

....

....

....

....

....

....

....

....

....

....

12

THE LITTLE THINGS I DID THIS WEEK

THE CHANGES I CAN SEE:

....
....
....
....
....
....
....
....
....
....

THE CHANGES I CAN FEEL:

....
....
....
....
....
....
....
....
....

12

13
WEEK

"You've no idea what a poor opinion I have of myself—and how little I deserve it."

—W. S. Gilbert

THIS WEEK'S MENTAL TIP

What image do you project to yourself and the world? Your body and how you carry yourself tells the world just how you feel about yourself on the inside. A fat, out-of-shape, lethargic body speaks the message loud and clear that you have a poor opinion of yourself and that eating right, exercising, and taking care of your body and mind aren't important because you are undeserving. But, change a few of those poor eating habits, become more active, and the new message it sends out for all to see will begin to change things in your life that will amaze you.

THIS WEEK'S EXERCISE TIP

For flabby triceps, try a dumbbell triceps kickback. Take a light dumbbell in one hand. With a slight bend at the knees, bend your upper body forward until it's at about a 90-degree angle with your legs. Place the upper arm holding the dumbbell against your side and bend your elbow so the dumbbell hangs down. Keeping your upper arm in the same position, bring your hand and the dumbbell back behind you until your arm is fully locked out. Feel it in the triceps (back of the arm)? You bet, but just wait. Do the same thing again, only this time, raise your upper arm higher so that your elbow is above your back (compared to your elbow just resting against your side). Now kick (extend) the dumbbell back until the arm is straight. Do three sets of ten to fifteen reps for each arm.

THIS WEEK'S NUTRITION TIP

Want a drink that can help you live longer? Green tea and red wine (light consumption of one to two glasses) may be your answer. Studies have shown that polyphenols—powerful antioxidants found in red wine and green tea—help fight cell damage from free radicals.

THE LITTLE THINGS I DID THIS WEEK

FOR NUTRITION:

FOR EXERCISE:

13

THE LITTLE THINGS I DID THIS WEEK

TO CHANGE MY THINKING:

....

....

....

....

....

....

....

....

....

TO HELP INSPIRE MYSELF:

....

....

....

....

....

....

....

....

13

THE LITTLE THINGS I DID THIS WEEK

THE CHANGES I CAN SEE:

....

....

....

....

....

....

....

....

....

....

THE CHANGES I CAN FEEL:

....

....

....

....

....

....

....

....

....

13

14
WEEK

"God will not look you over for medals, degrees, or diplomas, but for scars."

—ELBERT HUBBARD

THIS WEEK'S MENTAL TIP

Some of the toughest battles you'll ever face in life are with yourself: all the pain and suffering you may have faced or are still facing from all the failed diets and workout plans gone wrong. Maybe it was the lack of motivation to "stay with the program," or how hard you pushed yourself to experience success this time and show all your family and friends that you're serious, only to have things go wrong—again. Yet life has a way of neutralizing and healing those pains; it's called time and experience. All those experiences taught you some very valuable lessons. Getting in shape is not about competition, comparison, or proving anything to anyone else. It's about doing it because it's good for you, it's healthy for you, and it can help you live longer. Always remember that those who achieve greatness in any calling are those with deep scars and even deeper happiness.

THIS WEEK'S EXERCISE TIP

While waiting to cross the street, place your heels on the curb while allowing your toes to touch the street pavement. Raise the front of your shoes above curb level (or as high as possible) and repeat. These reverse toe raises are the secret to bringing out the best in your lower legs and can even help reduce ankle size, thereby giving your legs fantastic shape and appearance without even going to the gym. Do this each day and watch what happens in just ten days.

THIS WEEK'S NUTRITION TIP

Looking for a bag full of memory boosting? Try the produce section in the grocery store. Have a baked potato. It's loaded with memory-enhancing vitamin B_6.

THE LITTLE THINGS I DID THIS WEEK

FOR NUTRITION:

FOR EXERCISE:

THE LITTLE THINGS I DID THIS WEEK

TO CHANGE MY THINKING:

TO HELP INSPIRE MYSELF:

THE LITTLE THINGS I DID THIS WEEK

THE CHANGES I CAN SEE:

THE CHANGES I CAN FEEL:

WEEK

"It is by attempting to reach the top in a single leap that so much misery is caused in the world."

—WILLIAM CORBETT

THIS WEEK'S MENTAL TIP

Perhaps one of the toughest things about life is how hard we are on ourselves. Instead of starting off slowly with a new exercise program, finding your groove, and allowing your body to adjust, how many times have you done too much, overexercised, gotten too tired, and too sore, and therefore became quickly unmotivated to go through that again? Made you miserable, didn't it? We all have done it, so at least we're in good company. Next time, try this: Do only enough exercise to feel good to your body, but no more. Stop, even if you know you can do more. Next time, do a little bit more and stop again. Keep doing this until you've reached just the right amount of exercise for the right amount of time for your body and goals. You've got the rest of your life to enjoy looking and feeling great. No need to do it all in one day.

THIS WEEK'S EXERCISE TIP

The fencing shuffle mimics the back-and-forth and side-to-side moves of a fencer. It strengthens leg muscles and connective tissue and helps increase agility and lateral stability. Begin by standing straight up with a slight bend to the knees. Place your right or left foot forward (whichever feels most natural). Raise your heels to put more of your body weight on the balls of your feet. Move forward using only the momentum of your body leaning forward and springing off your toes. Your feet should come off the ground only a few inches as you move forward. Try going forward 6 to 12 inches and then spring back. Do the same thing to your left and right side and then come back. Begin by going a few inches and then increase the distance you move forward or backward and side-to-side as you get used to the movement.

THIS WEEK'S NUTRITION TIP

Are you a beef lover looking for the leanest cuts you can buy? Go for the round cuts such as round tip, top round, bottom round, eye of round, top loin, sirloin, and lean ground beef. And when it comes to ground beef, buy the darkest color the store has; the darker the red color, the leaner the beef.

THE LITTLE THINGS I DID THIS WEEK

FOR NUTRITION:

15

FOR EXERCISE:

THE LITTLE THINGS I DID THIS WEEK

15

TO CHANGE MY THINKING:

....
....
....
....
....
....
....
....
....
....

TO HELP INSPIRE MYSELF:

....
....
....
....
....
....
....
....
....

THE LITTLE THINGS I DID THIS WEEK

THE CHANGES I CAN SEE:

THE CHANGES I CAN FEEL:

15

16
WEEK

"The greatest thing about man is his ability to transcend himself, his ancestry, and his environment and to become what he dreams of being."

—TULLY C. KNOLES

THIS WEEK'S MENTAL TIP

You were born a blank slate when it comes to writing any dream in your heart and making it real in your life. You are an unlimited source of imagination and power when it comes to creating the life you want. But have you? And if not, why not? Think about this for a moment. Unless you're living that dream life of yours, one of the biggest reasons could be that you won't allow yourself to live it. You see, nowhere is it written that your life should or must fit the mold or expectations of what you think your family, friends, or society expects from you. They were given their lives to do with as they choose and you were given your life to be whomever and do whatever you choose. If your life was meant for others to decide, it would've been given to them and not to you, so break free from the lies that have held you back. Change your body. Change your life. Travel the world. Be a painter or a poet. Raise a family if you want. Be anything and everything you dream and start today. Nothing and no one can hold you back.

THIS WEEK'S EXERCISE TIP

Looking for a sure cure for the "I'm in a rut" blues? It's called the "Thirty-Day Push" and it can transform your body. Because your body quickly habituates (translation: gets used to doing the same thing), oftentimes you'll need not only to do something completely different but to do it in unconventional ways. If you've been working out doing the same kinds of exercises, with the same weight and reps, then what your body could use is something completely different. Try doing 50 percent fewer sets, 50 percent fewer exercises, but double your work-out intensity. That is, spend less time working out but lift heavier weights (only after a good warm-up) during the workout. When I say heavier, I'm not talking about an extra five or ten pounds. I'm talking about using near-maximum-ability weights for fewer reps, say three to six reps instead of ten to twelve. Be prepared to be a bit sore after each workout, but the soreness will quickly go away as your body breaks out of the rut and changes by making you stronger and firmer in areas you may have thought could not change. The key is to use this type of training and any other different types you'd like to try for the next thirty days and then go back to the maintenance program you were on before you started the Thirty-Day Push. You may find that doing the Thirty-Day Push every four months may be just the ticket to keep you progressing for years and years to come.

THIS WEEK'S NUTRITION TIP

When buying breads and grain foods, choose those that say "whole grain" on the label. Why? For one, it isn't overly processed and it still has all its natural ingredients. Whole grains also have higher fiber, which is good for that beautiful bod of yours.

THE LITTLE THINGS I DID THIS WEEK

FOR NUTRITION:

....

....

....

....

....

....

....

....

....

FOR EXERCISE:

....

....

....

....

....

....

....

....

16

THE LITTLE THINGS I DID THIS WEEK

TO CHANGE MY THINKING:

TO HELP INSPIRE MYSELF:

16

THE LITTLE THINGS I DID THIS WEEK

THE CHANGES I CAN SEE:

....
....
....
....
....
....
....
....
....

THE CHANGES I CAN FEEL:

....
....
....
....
....
....
....
....
....

16

WEEK 17

"At every crossing on the road that leads to the future, each progressive spirit is opposed by a thousand appointed to guard the past."

—MAURICE MAETERLINCK

THIS WEEK'S MENTAL TIP

You can bet that for any man or woman who desired a new kind of life, there was always someone who challenged them. Even with something so simple and positive as eating just a little bit healthier and doing just a little bit more exercise to change how they look and feel, other people may bring up many reasons why you cannot or should not do it. The fact is, most people are so afraid of changing any part of their lives that when someone with enough belief in themselves comes along and wants to make changes they are met with an army of disapproving looks, frowning faces, and words meant to deflate. If you've got the desire to change, then keep that head of yours looking forward and straight ahead and care not what anyone else says or thinks.

THIS WEEK'S EXERCISE TIP

Here's something you can do anywhere, anytime; it give you a potent mini-workout. I call it "tense and relax." Flex your arm until you feel the biceps contracting and tensing. Hold the biceps in that tensed position for anywhere from four to ten seconds. Really tense it as hard as you can for the entire four to ten seconds. Let that arm relax and do the same thing for the other arm. For the chest, put both arms straight out in front of you; don't allow them to touch as you squeeze the chest together. The trick is to keep the maximum amount of tension—for those four to ten seconds—on the muscle you want to work.

THIS WEEK'S NUTRITION TIP

Is there a way you can have chocolate and feel good about it, too? You bet. Try using unsweetened cocoa powder in recipes that call for unsweetened chocolate, Cocoa powder is chocolate but with most of the fat removed. And to sweeten things up, try adding some honey or applesauce.

THE LITTLE THINGS I DID THIS WEEK

FOR NUTRITION:

....

....

....

....

....

....

....

....

....

....

FOR EXERCISE:

....

....

....

....

....

....

....

....

....

....

17

THE LITTLE THINGS I DID THIS WEEK

TO CHANGE MY THINKING:

....

....

....

....

....

....

....

....

....

....

....

TO HELP INSPIRE MYSELF:

....

....

....

....

....

....

....

....

....

17

THE LITTLE THINGS I DID THIS WEEK

THE CHANGES I CAN SEE:

....

....

....

....

....

....

....

....

....

....

THE CHANGES I CAN FEEL:

....

....

....

....

....

....

....

....

....

17

18
WEEK

"The vision of things to be done may come a long time before the way of doing them becomes clear, but woe to him that distrusts the vision."

—JENKIN LLOYD JONES

THIS WEEK'S MENTAL TIP

In the midst of everything that happens in your life, you may be confused since it seems like you'll have no idea of what to do next or how
things will turn out. And in your seemingly endless search for the right
answer, you may get a feeling, an intuitive hunch—and often when
you least expect it—about the right thing to do. More times than not,
that hunch is the right answer and direction for you to follow. It comes
from deep inside your mind—away from the daily distractions—and
it's giving you the right direction and action you must take to solve a
problem or understand a situation and life lesson.

THIS WEEK'S EXERCISE TIP

Many people love snow skiing and I'm going to give you a terrific workout that you can do while doing it. Simply changing leg positions will be
all that's needed to get an amazing leg workout. Start out by keeping
your knees slightly bent as you ski. After a few hundred feet, bend your
legs even more and lower your body a few inches more. Hold your legs
in this position for at least two to three minutes, then return your legs
to the starting position. The more your legs approach the straight up-
and-down position, the less resistance and the easier it is. However, the
more you bend your legs—three-quarters of your range is terrific—and
lower your body (up to the point of the seated position where resistance then becomes lessened), the harder it will be. Do combinations of
low resistance with minimal leg bend to high resistance with lots of leg
bend for a day on the slopes your legs and body will not soon forget.

THIS WEEK'S NUTRITION TIP

If you've got a hankerin' for a good old-fashioned hot dog, go for the
low-fat and nonfat turkey or chicken franks.

THE LITTLE THINGS I DID THIS WEEK

FOR NUTRITION:

....

....

....

....

....

....

....

....

....

FOR EXERCISE:

....

....

....

....

....

....

....

....

18

THE LITTLE THINGS I DID THIS WEEK

TO CHANGE MY THINKING:

....

....

....

....

....

....

....

....

....

....

18

TO HELP INSPIRE MYSELF:

....

....

....

....

....

....

....

....

....

THE LITTLE THINGS I DID THIS WEEK

THE CHANGES I CAN SEE:

THE CHANGES I CAN FEEL:

18

19
WEEK

"Careful and wise is the person who pauses before changing his life or making his plans based on the promises of others."

—Robert Wolff

THIS WEEK'S MENTAL TIP

Others mean well. They tell us things, promise us things, and want to give us things, but many times they don't come through. After all, they experience the same thing from other people, so who can blame them for things they cannot control? It's almost like an endless chain connecting people and events in the movie of life. When it happens to others, it's easy to chalk it up as "human nature," except when it becomes your happiness that is staked on other people's promises and actions. Take having a workout partner. You tell each other if you exercise with me or start that new diet, then I'll do it, too. So, you get all happy and excited, and lo and behold, that day comes when she can't do it or forgets to meet you for a workout. After all, she promised, but life happens and plans and people change. It happens every day, so just understand it for what it is and let it go. You've learned a powerful lesson, and that is, when it comes to changing or experiencing anything in your life, the only one you can depend on 100 percent of the time is you! If others want to share in those experiences, that's great. But with or without anyone, simply live your life, look and feel the way you want, and depend on yourself, and you will not be disappointed.

THIS WEEK'S EXERCISE TIP

If you love the water and are looking for an awesome cross-training workout, then rowing is your answer. Besides cross-country skiing, rowing ranks right near the top for one of the most effective aerobic and resistance exercises you can do. There are a few things to keep in mind to get great results. Number one: Big, long, and sweeping strokes demand briefer, more intense bursts of strength to overcome the added resistance of the rowing movement. This is a good way to take care of the resistance part of the workout. Number two: Short and quick strokes may not require the quick power surges needed to move the paddles through the larger amounts of water and greater distance, but they do require more endurance for the increased number of strokes needed to move you and the boat over the same distance. This is a great way to train for the aerobic/cardio portion of your workout. When you combine both, you get a marvelous way to condition your body.

THIS WEEK'S NUTRITION TIP

Many people are confused when they hear they should be eating a certain number of servings of this or that food or from a particular food group. So, do you know how big a serving is? Here's an easy way: One-half to one cup of cooked or raw vegetables is one serving, one-half cup of vegetable or fruit juice is one serving, and one medium-size piece of fruit is also one serving. And what about portion sizes for fish, fowl, or meat? Go for a serving (about 3 to 4 ounces) that's about the size of a computer mouse or folded wallet.

THE LITTLE THINGS I DID THIS WEEK

FOR NUTRITION:

....

....

....

....

....

....

....

....

FOR EXERCISE:

....

....

....

....

....

....

....

....

19

THE LITTLE THINGS I DID THIS WEEK

TO CHANGE MY THINKING:

TO HELP INSPIRE MYSELF:

19

THE LITTLE THINGS I DID THIS WEEK

THE CHANGES I CAN SEE:

19

THE CHANGES I CAN FEEL:

20
WEEK

"My mother said to me, 'If you become a soldier
you'll be a general; if you become a monk you'll
end up as the pope.' Instead, I became a painter
and wound up as Picasso."

—PABLO PICASSO

THIS WEEK'S MENTAL TIP

I love that quote because it says to me that if we follow the calling of our lives, use the desires we have and the talents inside us, then we can become Picassos in whatever we do. Follow those desires and dreams and allow them to fill your life with the incredible abundance of experiences and rewards waiting for you right now. No matter who you are, where you live, how young or old, short or tall, or your color or creed, you are a Picasso right now. Follow your heart and dreams wherever they lead you.

THIS WEEK'S EXERCISE TIP

As they say, human nature tends to be on the lazy side. So, if you're looking for a novel way to get a light workout, look to your refrigerator. You're going to need two gallon jugs of either juice, milk, or water. Hold each of those gallon jugs in your hands and think of them like dumbbells in the gym. Give yourself a quickie arm pump by doing a fast set of twenty-five reps. How about raising and lowering the jugs out to your sides for twelve reps for a nice little delt (shoulder) pump. Do this either early in the morning before breakfast or before dinner and you may find that, while this may not radically change your body, it will get the blood pumping, and many times that's enough to release those powerful exercise-produced endorphins that de-stress you and invigorate your mind and body.

THIS WEEK'S NUTRITION TIP

Did you know that a 4-ounce serving of french fries has almost three times the calories and more than ten times the waist-expanding amount of fat as the same size 4-ounce baked potato? If you love french fries, try baking them instead of frying. That way you get great taste with minimal fat.

THE LITTLE THINGS I DID THIS WEEK

FOR NUTRITION:

....

....

....

....

....

....

....

....

....

20

FOR EXERCISE:

....

....

....

....

....

....

....

....

....

THE LITTLE THINGS I DID THIS WEEK

TO CHANGE MY THINKING:

....

....

....

....

....

....

....

....

20

TO HELP INSPIRE MYSELF:

....

....

....

....

....

....

....

....

THE LITTLE THINGS I DID THIS WEEK

THE CHANGES I CAN SEE:

THE CHANGES I CAN FEEL:

20

21
WEEK

"I am not interested in the past. I am interested in the future, for that is where I expect to spend the rest of my life."

—CHARLES F. KETTERING

THIS WEEK'S MENTAL TIP

Why do you think it's so hard for people to let go of the past? And why is it so unnecessarily tough for people to let go of the false ideas and myths about their bodies? For example, a person looks and feels a certain way for a number of years, has tried numerous diets, bought lots of exercise gizmos and machines, and still, they always go back to looking and feeling like their old selves. So what's wrong here? A big reason is that they still have the same old picture of how they are supposed to look floating inside their head and along with that, the limiting beliefs about themselves that keep that picture alive, day after day, year after frustrating year. It's time to change that. From this day on, one of the most powerful things you can do to change how you look and feel is to first give your brain a new picture on the *inside* that you want it to create on the *outside*. All lasting changes must *first* come from inside before they show up on the *outside*. Along with that new picture of how you want to look, think more and more each day about how great and happy you'll feel once that new picture of you actually begins to happen. You'll find yourself starting to feel good about yourself again and it really will start to sink in that yes, this new you is really going to happen. And believe me, it most certainly will!

THIS WEEK'S EXERCISE TIP

One exercise that's just as good today as it was when you were a kid is cycling. In gyms cycling machines are all over the place; you may even have one at home. But the real fun of cycling is when you're doing it outdoors. Here are a few ways to change the look of your legs simply by changing how you cycle. First, if you want thinner and leaner thighs, simply using higher gears when you pedal will create less resistance and easier, yet faster strokes. If you're wanting more muscular legs, then spend more time using the lower gears of the bike, which will create more resistance and slower strokes.

THIS WEEK'S NUTRITION TIP

Many people love carbohydrates, and granted, they are important for energy. However, excess carbohydrates can be a real no-no if you're wanting a leaner and more shapely body. Excess carbohydrates, eating more than your body needs—yes, even those sweet treats that have "fat free" on the label—are stored as fat. When the body breaks down carbohydrates for its use, they eventually form pyruvic acid and this puts a damper on how the body uses and gets rid of body fat. Eating too many carbohydrates (especially the wrong kinds of empty calorie foods made with white sugar) can cause B vitamin deficiency as the body uses its B vitamins in order to process the carbohydrates. The best kinds of carbohydrates to eat are fresh vegetables, fresh fruits, and whole grains and cereals. Just be careful that you don't eat too many of them.

THE LITTLE THINGS I DID THIS WEEK

FOR NUTRITION:

....

....

....

....

....

....

....

....

....

FOR EXERCISE:

....

....

....

....

....

....

....

....

....

21

THE LITTLE THINGS I DID THIS WEEK

TO CHANGE MY THINKING:

TO HELP INSPIRE MYSELF:

THE LITTLE THINGS I DID THIS WEEK

THE CHANGES I CAN SEE:

....

....

....

....

....

....

....

....

....

....

....

....

THE CHANGES I CAN FEEL:

21

....

....

....

....

....

....

....

....

....

....

22
WEEK

"If we were to do all that we are capable of doing, we would literally astonish ourselves."

—Thomas A. Edison

THIS WEEK'S MENTAL TIP

Ever thought about what you are truly capable of achieving and doing? Not what you have done in the past or are doing now, I'm talking about your untapped potential. Society and most family and friends are used to doing just enough at their jobs, at school, in relationships, or at anything else to keep things going smoothly. After all, they reason, why do more if you don't need to? And that's the rub. Little do they know that only a little bit more knowledge, a little bit more belief, and a little more effort is often the biggest thing that separates someone who rises to the top from the rest. Here's a wee bit of change-your-life advice: Do just a little bit more than you're doing now, in any area of your life, and the results just might astonish you. The difference between the race horse that wins the big prize and the second-place finisher is often a split second.

THIS WEEK'S EXERCISE TIP

Ever dream you could get in better shape each time you shop? That's got to be the best of both worlds! A very simple way to get your heart pumping, blood flowing, and muscles working is by increasing the amount of walking you'd normally do during any given day. When you arrive at the mall, office, restaurant, theater, school, or anywhere else, simply park the car farther away. Next, when leaving wherever else, try using the opposite entrance you came in. The extra distance can make a big difference. Finally, when given a choice of stairs or the escalator, always use the stairs.

THIS WEEK'S NUTRITION TIP

You know that a good diet helps keep you healthy and a bad diet does just the opposite. You also have a good idea, without reading book after book or seeing a nutritional guru, which foods are good for your body and which ones make it sluggish. What you may not know is which kinds of foods give your body the extra power of antioxidants (those little warriors that help keep your body healthy). Here are a few to eat more of:

- Fresh fruits and vegetables are best—the darker the colors the better—and next on the list would be the frozen varieties.
- Go for the fruits over the juices.
- Pick red grapes over green ones.
- Eat more raw vegetables like broccoli and cauliflower.
- When cooking, use extra virgin olive oil.
- Eat more yellow or red onions.
- Choose pink grapefruit and not white.

THE LITTLE THINGS I DID THIS WEEK

FOR NUTRITION:

....

....

....

....

....

....

....

....

....

....

FOR EXERCISE:

....

22

....

....

....

....

....

....

....

....

THE LITTLE THINGS I DID THIS WEEK

TO CHANGE MY THINKING:

....

....

....

....

....

....

....

....

TO HELP INSPIRE MYSELF:

....

....

....

....

....

....

....

....

22

THE LITTLE THINGS I DID THIS WEEK

THE CHANGES I CAN SEE:

THE CHANGES I CAN FEEL:

22

23
WEEK

"Success is to be measured not so much by the position that one has reached in life as by the obstacles which he has overcome while trying to succeed."

—BOOKER T. WASHINGTON

THIS WEEK'S MENTAL TIP

Adversity, hardship, pain, and discomfort are incredibly powerful forces that transform us. If you're experiencing any of them right now, then there's much to be happy about, for all of those things are changing you—changing your beliefs, changing your attitudes, changing your discipline, changing your actions, and changing your body and life to be something better, something more. Great workouts that build a great body come from the experiences gained from less-than-great workouts when you start out. You overcome the obstacles and sticking points by weeding out the things that don't work, to find the things that do.

THIS WEEK'S EXERCISE TIP

Traveling can be a real detour to even the best exercise plans. When you're on a plane, drink more water. Some experts say a person's body loses one pint of water for every hour they are flying due to cabin pressure and processed air. Alcohol is also a big factor in dehydration, so if you're having a drink, have an equal amount of water. Eat less salty foods and snacks. Every thirty minutes or so, get out of your seat and walk up and down the aisle. Sitting in a cramped seat with your legs bent doesn't do your body any favors, so when seated, do some heel lifts (e.g., calf raises) and extend those legs straight out in front of you (if you can).

THIS WEEK'S NUTRITION TIP

One tablespoon of brewer's yeast will give you seventeen vitamins (even all those B vitamins), fourteen minerals (including those trace minerals), and sixteen amino acids—and it's only about twenty to twenty-five calories. You can put it on cereal, yogurt, cottage cheese, or salads.

THE LITTLE THINGS I DID THIS WEEK

FOR NUTRITION:

....

....

....

....

....

....

....

....

....

....

FOR EXERCISE:

....

....

....

....

....

....

....

....

....

23

THE LITTLE THINGS I DID THIS WEEK

TO CHANGE MY THINKING:

....
....
....
....
....
....
....
....
....
....
....

TO HELP INSPIRE MYSELF:

....
....
....
....
....
....
....
....
....
....

23

THE LITTLE THINGS I DID THIS WEEK

THE CHANGES I CAN SEE:

....

....

....

....

....

....

....

....

....

....

THE CHANGES I CAN FEEL:

....

....

....

....

....

....

....

....

23

24
WEEK

"*Nurture great thoughts, for you will never go higher than your thoughts.*"

—Benjamin Disraeli

THIS WEEK'S MENTAL TIP

"Where the mind goes, the body follows" is a maxim I've found to be 100 percent true. You and I can only go as high as our thoughts and our beliefs in ourselves. And who sets the limits on those beliefs? We do. Beliefs come from our thoughts; for what we think about, we most certainly bring about. If you believe that you'll always be overweight, out of shape, and look and feel the same, then those thoughts become your limits and you'll never go beyond those boundaries unless and until you change those thoughts to match the changes you want to see happen, the new image of how you want to look and feel.

THIS WEEK'S EXERCISE TIP

Last week, we talked about what you can do on the plane. So what do you do once you arrive at your destination? Depending on when you arrive (many international flights arrive the next morning), you'll want to stay awake during the day and make your bedtime at night, even if it's as early as 7:00 This will help keep your body clock in its regular awake/day–sleep/night mode. After checking in to your destination, and as soon as possible, either do a bit of light exercise in your hotel room or, better yet, go for a relaxing sightseeing walk around the city. Just stay active and keep moving as much as you enjoyably can. Eat light meals throughout the day; having high-fat or high-calorie meals will only make you tired. Some people on long international flights have found melatonin to be a good way to knock off the effects of jet lag, some say by as much as a few days. About ninety minutes or so before bedtime, you might try having a light meal with a bit more protein. As a tired traveler, you sure don't want a hungry, growling stomach to wake you up in the middle of the night and make it difficult for you to become tired again and fall back to sleep.

THIS WEEK'S NUTRITION TIP

Every so often, it's not uncommon to get an upset stomach, and many of the foods you eat and drink (such as salty and fried foods, mayonnaise, fruit juices, coffee, and meat) can be likely culprits. For years, people have believed eating a banana a day helps calm the queezies, so you might want to give that a try. Others swear by tea. Another great natural way to soothe an upset tummy or even motion sickness is by taking ginger. Some say ginger snap cookies do the trick. Now you know why Grandma and Mom gave you a little ginger ale when you had that upset tum-tum.

THE LITTLE THINGS I DID THIS WEEK

FOR NUTRITION:

FOR EXERCISE:

THE LITTLE THINGS I DID THIS WEEK

TO CHANGE MY THINKING:

....

....

....

....

....

....

....

....

....

....

....

....

....

TO HELP INSPIRE MYSELF:

....

....

....

....

....

....

....

....

....

....

....

24

THE LITTLE THINGS I DID THIS WEEK

THE CHANGES I CAN SEE:

....

....

....

....

....

....

....

....

....

THE CHANGES I CAN FEEL:

....

....

....

....

....

....

....

....

24

25 WEEK

"*I am an old man and have known a great many troubles, but most of them never happened.*"

—MARK TWAIN

THIS WEEK'S MENTAL TIP

A very wise person once said, "The majority of things in life we worry about never happen, and the very few things that do are, nine times out of ten, either beyond our control or they're not as bad as they seem." So forget worrying. Life's much too short to waste time thinking about things that most likely will never happen.

THIS WEEK'S EXERCISE TIP

Remember those big beach or gym balls you used to hit around when you were a kid? Well, they're also excellent at toning the abs and lower back. You'll want to use one that's at least two to three feet in diameter. Place the ball on the floor and center the middle of your back over it. Keep your glutes against the ball and your legs spread apart about one to two feet. Keep your feet firmly planted on the floor about two to three feet apart. Cross your arms across your chest and keep your head up. Slowly raise your upper body toward your legs for a few inches; hold it there for one to two seconds and slowly lower it back down and begin again without stopping at the bottom of the exercise. Do at least fifteen to twenty-five reps.

THIS WEEK'S NUTRITION TIP

Here's a little trick you can use to fool your brain into thinking you've eaten more than you actually have and it can work great for dropping those extra fat pounds. Try using smaller plates and utensils. Not only will it reduce the amount of food you can put on them at any given time, you'll have to take more bites just to get the same portions you normally would. Try eating more slowly. Many times, we eat so fast that we keep eating when our bodies are already full, yet the signal from the stomach to the brain hasn't had enough time to catch up and tell us to stop.

THE LITTLE THINGS I DID THIS WEEK

FOR NUTRITION:

....

....

....

....

....

....

....

....

....

....

....

FOR EXERCISE:

....

....

....

....

....

....

....

....

....

25

THE LITTLE THINGS I DID THIS WEEK

TO CHANGE MY THINKING:

....
....
....
....
....
....
....
....
....
....
....

TO HELP INSPIRE MYSELF:

....
....
....
....
....
....
....
....
....

25

THE LITTLE THINGS I DID THIS WEEK

THE CHANGES I CAN SEE:

....

....

....

....

....

....

....

....

....

THE CHANGES I CAN FEEL:

....

....

....

....

....

....

....

25

....

....

26
WEEK

"If you wait for the perfect moment when all is safe and assured, it may never arrive. Mountains will not be climbed, races won, or lasting happiness achieved."

—MAURICE CHEVALIER

THIS WEEK'S MENTAL TIP

There will never be a more perfect time to change your body and your life than right now. There will not be a time when you'll know all the uncertainties and difficulties that await you. And there will not be a time when you'll know all the happiness and rewards that are waiting for you. All you have is today, right now, this moment. You don't know what's going to happen in the next hour, let alone the next day or year. Right now is yours and it's all you've got. Grab it and make it exactly what you want.

THIS WEEK'S EXERCISE TIP

This week, we're still having a ball (as in exercise ball) and I'll tell you how to use it to strengthen the lower back. Using the same size ball as last week, place the front of your body over the ball. Be sure only the stomach and upper thighs touch the ball. You don't want to have the ball touching the chest or neck. Spread your legs out wide—about 2 to 4 feet—and keep your toes touching the floor at all times. Clasp your hands and place them and your arms behind your head. Slowly raise your upper body a few inches, hold it there for one to two seconds, slowly lower it back down, and begin again. Be sure not to overextend the upper body by raising it too far or too fast. Slow, steady, and controlled movement is what you want. Do three sets of five to nine reps once a week.

THIS WEEK'S NUTRITION TIP

If you love being active and want to eat foods that will be good for those joints, then start eating more fish foods high in omega-3 fatty acids such as salmon, mackerel, trout, and sardines.

THE LITTLE THINGS I DID THIS WEEK

FOR NUTRITION:

....

....

....

....

....

....

....

....

....

FOR EXERCISE:

....

....

....

....

....

....

....

....

26

THE LITTLE THINGS I DID THIS WEEK

TO CHANGE MY THINKING:

....

....

....

....

....

....

....

....

....

....

....

TO HELP INSPIRE MYSELF:

....

....

....

....

....

....

....

....

....

26

THE LITTLE THINGS I DID THIS WEEK

THE CHANGES I CAN SEE:

....

....

....

....

....

....

....

....

....

....

....

THE CHANGES I CAN FEEL:

....

....

....

....

....

....

....

....

....

26

27
WEEK

"I love you for what you are, but I love you yet more for what you are going to be. I love you not so much for your realities as for your ideals. I pray for your desires that they may be great, rather than for your satisfactions, which may be so hazardously little."

—CARL SANDBURG

THIS WEEK'S MENTAL TIP

On the one hand, some people say much of our problems as men and women come from not being satisfied with what we have and always wanting more. On the other hand, some say our problems lie in settling for less than we are capable of. So who's right? Are any of them? A good rule of thumb I've found is a simple test: If you look outside yourself for happiness and validation in people and material things, then happiness and fulfillment will elude you. If you are essentially a happy person with or without the accolades of worldly success or the need to possess and acquire things, then your desire to grow, expand, become, and experience can bring you even greater happiness. Now, let's look at your dream and goal of a new-looking and better-feeling body. It's only human to think that once you reach your goal, you'll have all you need or want. But when you reach your goal of a changed body and a changed you, which you most certainly will, then a brand-new road will open up that you never could've imagined when you started, and from which new goals and dreams can begin. This is the beautiful dance of life and one you'll deeply enjoy. Just be sure your head and heart are in the right place and you'll have a lifetime of enjoyment.

THIS WEEK'S EXERCISE TIP

Using the stairs can be a great way to work out. One way is to do lunges. Lunges are a terrific leg exercise and will work wonders to shape, tone, and strengthen your thighs. Begin by placing one leg on the first step and the other leg in line under your upper body. Look forward, keep the upper body erect, and allow the leg under your body to bend. Start off by lowering the body for a few inches; then go back up to the starting position. After a few reps, lower the leg and knee (that are under your body) until the knee is only a few inches above the floor. Do ten to twenty reps for each leg. To make it a tougher workout, put the leg in front of you that you are working on the second or third stair. And the farther the nonworking leg is from the other leg, the more difficult the exercise becomes.

THIS WEEK'S NUTRITION TIP

You work hard at school, your career, raising family, enjoying life, and staying fit and healthy, yet, for many people, the sight of varicose veins in the legs doesn't bring a smile. So can you do anything to help prevent or minimize those pesky things? First, check to be sure you're getting enough vitamin E in your diet since vitamin E acts as a blood vessel dilator and helps keep circulation moving freely and smoothly. And when it's time to relax, give that body a rest, but don't relax sitting up. Lie down and elevate your feet so they are slightly higher than your head.

THE LITTLE THINGS I DID THIS WEEK

FOR NUTRITION:

FOR EXERCISE:

THE LITTLE THINGS I DID THIS WEEK

TO CHANGE MY THINKING:

TO HELP INSPIRE MYSELF:

THE LITTLE THINGS I DID THIS WEEK

THE CHANGES I CAN SEE:

THE CHANGES I CAN FEEL:

28
WEEK

"Ideals are like stars; you will not succeed in touching them with your hands, but like the seafaring man on the desert of waters, you choose them as your guides, and, following them, you reach your destiny."

—CARL SCHURZ

THIS WEEK'S MENTAL TIP

I can tell you with absolute certainty that the path you think you'll be taking when you begin your journey to change your body and life will turn out to be amazingly different once you reach that goal. Look back at what has happened in your life and where you were just twelve months ago and look at where you are and who you are today. Talk about changes. And it's the same thing that's going to happen to you when you begin exercising and being more active again or getting back to eating more healthfully and treating your body better. Always keep in mind the goal and the dream; keep looking to them as your guide, like the stars in the sky at night as you begin traveling down your new road to your dream. But always know that the road you take will not be a straight one and will have many hills, bumps, curves, potholes, and twists before you reach that point, just over the horizon, when you arrive at the destination of a new you and a new life.

THIS WEEK'S EXERCISE TIP

We're not finished "stairing" yet. Here are a few other ways to make the stairs your gym away from the gym. First, when walking up the stairs, try taking two or three stairs at a time instead of the usual one. Next, try going up the stairs sideways and backward. You'll feel this work the leg muscles differently. To increase endurance and aerobic benefits, try brisk walking up and down the stairs. When that becomes easy, start doing a slow run up the stairs followed by a regular walk down them. To get an even better workout, you can increase the speed of your walk or run up the stairs, run up more stairs, or do fewer stairs but do them faster and more often.

THIS WEEK'S NUTRITION TIP

If you are taking calcium and iron supplements, don't take them at the same time. Taking them at the same time causes an interaction that prevents the body from absorbing the iron. Drinks such as coffee and tea also get in the way of absorption. However, orange or tomato juice helps the body absorb that iron. Try taking the iron supplement with your meal or with tomato or orange juice and then take the calcium supplement sixty to ninety minutes later.

THE LITTLE THINGS I DID THIS WEEK

FOR NUTRITION:

28

FOR EXERCISE:

THE LITTLE THINGS I DID THIS WEEK

28

TO CHANGE MY THINKING:

TO HELP INSPIRE MYSELF:

THE LITTLE THINGS I DID THIS WEEK

THE CHANGES I CAN SEE:

....

....

....

....

....

....

....

....

....

THE CHANGES I CAN FEEL:

....

....

....

....

....

....

....

....

....

28

29
WEEK

"No man ever became great or good except through many and great mistakes."

—WILLIAM GLADSTONE

THIS WEEK'S MENTAL TIP

When I began working out, I made about every mistake there was to make. I worked out too hard, too much, and too often. I listened to everyone but me as to what was the best exercise program for me. Yet, it was through those mistakes that I began getting frustrated at not only my lack of progress, but not following my instincts of knowing what I needed to do, when and how I needed to do it, and then just doing it. Once I realized my mistakes, I quickly changed my actions, listened to myself, and followed my own road and the results and success I realized have been wonderful. Never fear making mistakes. Rather, I'd say, fear not making any.

THIS WEEK'S EXERCISE TIP

If you've been looking for a great way to shape, firm, and tone those outer thighs that you can do at home without any equipment, then this is for you. They're side leg raises and you do them three ways. First, with knees bent: Stand up straight and hold on to either the wall, doorknob, or stair rail for balance and support. With the right leg and foot on the floor, bend the left knee so your left foot is behind you and the leg you are lifting is in an L-shape. Keep the left upper leg in a straight line with your body. Raise that left leg up and out to your side as high as you can. Hold it at the top for one to two seconds, then slowly bring the leg back down and repeat. Do it for fifteen reps; then do the same thing for the other leg. Next, bend the knee at approximately three-fourths extension—that is, slightly bent and not fully extended. Do the same movement for the same number of reps. And last but not least, do the exercise with your legs straight and locked. You'll find this last way to be the most difficult of all, and you may not be able to lift your leg as high as you did the other two ways, but that's okay. Just raise it up and out to your side as high as you can and keep those reps going until you're finished.

THIS WEEK'S NUTRITION TIP

You've heard for years that people swear by vitamin C as a cheap way to get over a cold. But did you know a little supplement you can buy at your health food store called zinc gluconate with glycine may also do the trick? A Dartmouth University study showed this supplement knocked out a cold more than 40 percent faster.

THE LITTLE THINGS I DID THIS WEEK

FOR NUTRITION:

FOR EXERCISE:

29

THE LITTLE THINGS I DID THIS WEEK

TO CHANGE MY THINKING:

....
....
....
....
....
....
....
....
....
....

TO HELP INSPIRE MYSELF:

....
....
....
....
....
....
....
....
....

29

THE LITTLE THINGS I DID THIS WEEK

THE CHANGES I CAN SEE:

....

....

....

....

....

....

....

....

....

....

....

....

....

....

THE CHANGES I CAN FEEL:

....

....

....

....

....

....

....

....

....

....

29

30
WEEK

"Cease to inquire what the future has in store, and take as a gift whatever the day brings forth."

—Horace

THIS WEEK'S MENTAL TIP

Today, you may have a great workout and eat the ideal foods, and yet tomorrow, your workout and diet may be the pits. Instead of letting those not-so-good days get the best of you, let them go, and just do the best you can regardless of the results. Enjoy either working out or not working out, eating healthy or not eating healthy, or anything else that comes your way.

THIS WEEK'S EXERCISE TIP

What would you think if you could get really good at whatever sport or activity you enjoy, without having to actually do it? Ever watch a boxer act like he or she was boxing, doing all the punches and making all the foot and body moves, without any gloves on or an opponent in front of them? They were shadow practicing and it helps them tremendously to prepare for the real event. Basketball players do it, too. In fact, researchers did a study that compared one group who shot baskets each day to another who only practiced shooting baskets mentally to a third group who did nothing. The group that did nothing didn't improve. However, the group that simply practiced mentally shooting baskets had nearly the same results as those who actually physically did it! So, if you want to improve your game, whatever it may be, give shadow practicing a try.

THIS WEEK'S NUTRITION TIP

You say you just ate those foods that cause cavities and don't have your Listerine close by? Drink some tea; it's a powerful anticavity drink. You can also swig down milk, coffee, grape juice, or black cherry juice. As for anticavity foods, go for the cheeses such as Swiss, Brie, Monterey, Gouda, cheddar, mozzarella, or Jack.

THE LITTLE THINGS I DID THIS WEEK

FOR NUTRITION:

30

FOR EXERCISE:

THE LITTLE THINGS I DID THIS WEEK

TO CHANGE MY THINKING:

....
....
....
....
....
....
....
....
....
....
....
....

30

TO HELP INSPIRE MYSELF:

....
....
....
....
....
....
....
....
....
....
....

THE LITTLE THINGS I DID THIS WEEK

THE CHANGES I CAN SEE:

....

....

....

....

....

....

....

....

....

....

....

THE CHANGES I CAN FEEL:

....

....

....

....

....

....

....

....

....

30

31
WEEK

"If you have been wise and successful I congratulate you; unless you are unable to forget how successful you have been, then I pity you."

—Napoleon Hill

THIS WEEK'S MENTAL TIP

Every day, and for the rest of your life, always stay humble and keep learning. The ancients have a philosophy about those who do not. They are like a cup that is too full and quickly grows stagnant. As long as the cup stays empty, fresh water can be poured into it, and it will never go stale.

THIS WEEK'S EXERCISE TIP

The stair stepper is one of the most frequently used machines in the gym. Too bad a lot of people don't do it right. How many people do you see on the stepper either leaning over or holding on to the side rails (many of them with palms facing away from them) or doing these little chicken steps so their legs and feet are only moving a few inches up and down? All wrong. The way to get the most from any stair stepper is to place only the balls of the feet on the step platform, keep the body upright without bending over, hold on to the hand rails (only if you need support) with just your fingertips (better still, don't hold onto the rails at all), and take big, full, and deep steps that are all the way up and all the way down. Do it this way and you'll feel the difference.

THIS WEEK'S NUTRITION TIP

Think of how many times a day you use your teeth. When you multiply that over a lifetime, it's bound to amaze you how strong and resilient those teeth and gums are. To keep them that way for the rest of your life, brush and floss at least twice each day. Next, to keep those bones strong, be sure to get at least 1,000 milligrams of calcium (from either lowfat or nonfat yogurt, cottage cheese, skim milk, salmon, or canned sardines) each day, and keep that vitamin C intake high. That means either eating red and green peppers, strawberries, oranges and other citrus fruits, broccoli, tomatoes, or taking a vitamin C supplement.

THE LITTLE THINGS I DID THIS WEEK

FOR NUTRITION:

....

....

....

....

....

....

....

....

....

....

FOR EXERCISE:

....

....

....

....

....

....

....

....

....

THE LITTLE THINGS I DID THIS WEEK

TO CHANGE MY THINKING:

....

....

....

....

....

....

....

....

....

....

....

TO HELP INSPIRE MYSELF:

....

....

....

....

....

....

....

....

....

....

....

31

THE LITTLE THINGS I DID THIS WEEK

THE CHANGES I CAN SEE:

....
....
....
....
....
....
....
....
....
....

THE CHANGES I CAN FEEL:

....
....
....
....
....
....
....
....
....

31

WEEK 32

"*I cannot give you the formula for success, but I can give you the formula for failure—try to please everybody.*"

—HERBERT BAYARD SWOPE

THIS WEEK'S MENTAL TIP

I cannot tell you how many times people have told me how miserable they felt after telling others what they were going to do, only to have the fires of their new goals and dreams smothered by the cold water of negative reaction. Find and follow "your" formula for success and keep it a secret. And remember the old saying, "Tell the world what you're going to do, but first show it."

THIS WEEK'S EXERCISE TIP

In giving you our little stair-stepper tips from last week, you didn't think I would leave out the treadmill, did you? Say no more. More people have treadmills in their homes than stair steppers, so pay attention. Here's how to get even better results from walking on the mill. First, take long strides. Short strides don't make the muscles work like the big, long strides. Next, elevate the platform so you'll be walking on a slight-to-moderate incline. When you combine the long strides with a higher angle, you're entering "amazing results territory." Increase the speed of your walk. Walking at 3.3 mph or less really doesn't do as much to change your body as a faster gait of 3.3 mph or faster. Finally, don't hold on to those side or front hand rails. Swing those arms backward and forward as you walk and really put your entire body into the exercise. The more muscles you can work, the better your result will be.

THIS WEEK'S NUTRITION TIP

When traveling and dining out, make these food words your best friends: steamed, lean, baked, poached, grilled, roasted, fresh, and natural. Eat clean if you want to be lean.

THE LITTLE THINGS I DID THIS WEEK

FOR NUTRITION:

....

....

....

....

....

....

....

32

....

....

FOR EXERCISE:

....

....

....

....

....

....

....

....

THE LITTLE THINGS I DID THIS WEEK

TO CHANGE MY THINKING:

....

....

....

....

....

....

....

....

....

TO HELP INSPIRE MYSELF:

....

....

....

....

....

....

....

....

32

THE LITTLE THINGS I DID THIS WEEK

THE CHANGES I CAN SEE:

THE CHANGES I CAN FEEL:

33
WEEK

"If people only knew how hard I worked to gain mastery, it wouldn't seem so wonderful at all."

—MICHELANGELO

THIS WEEK'S MENTAL TIP

Turn on the television and watch any sports star, movie star, famous singer, or musician—they make what they do appear so easy that anyone can do it. And perhaps that's the deception, for the masters of their art and craft make the difficult seem simple. Yet, when you read stories about their lives, you'll find that their overnight success was twenty years or more in the making, and for many, it's taken an entire lifetime of heartache, frustration, isolation, doubt, discipline, incredible joys, and numbing pain to reach the pinnacle in their field. And to think you were bummed out and thinking about quitting when you had a not-so-good workout or the diet went off-track. Puts things in perspective now, doesn't it?

THIS WEEK'S EXERCISE TIP

Here's a great leg exercise (hits inner and outer thighs) you can do while sitting on the couch watching TV and all you'll need is a cheap little beach ball. Start off by placing the ball between your legs just above your knees. Squeeze the ball and hold it for three seconds; then relax. Do it twelve more times just like that. Next, move the ball down so it's centered between your knees. Squeeze and hold it for three seconds; then do twelve more reps. Bring the ball down your legs and let it rest between your upper calves and knees. Do the same reps and three-second squeezes. Finally, hold the ball between your ankle and calves and again do a three-second squeeze and hold; then do twelve more reps. You've just had a wonderful little leg workout without leaving your seat.

THIS WEEK'S NUTRITION TIP

When the cares of the world are getting the best of you and you're feeling that blood pressure begin to rise, stop for a moment, chill out, take ten deep breaths, and relax. Next, cut back on your sodium intake, especially from those processed, packaged, and canned foods. Drop a few pounds, cut back on the beer, keep doing the exercises in this book, and eat more potassium and magnesium from magnesium-rich foods such as lima beans, nuts, peas, seafood, and spinach and from potassium-rich foods such as cabbage, broccoli, spinach, bananas, potatoes, corn, and even orange juice.

THE LITTLE THINGS I DID THIS WEEK

FOR NUTRITION:

FOR EXERCISE:

33

THE LITTLE THINGS I DID THIS WEEK

TO CHANGE MY THINKING:

....

....

....

....

....

....

....

....

33

TO HELP INSPIRE MYSELF:

....

....

....

....

....

....

....

....

THE LITTLE THINGS I DID THIS WEEK

THE CHANGES I CAN SEE:

....
....
....
....
....
....
....
....
....
....

THE CHANGES I CAN FEEL:

....
....
....
....
....
....
....
....
....

33

34
WEEK

"When a person finds himself, when he stops imitating and envying others, there is something in his nature that says to him, 'This is it. You've found your road at last.'"

—Earl Nightingale

THIS WEEK'S MENTAL TIP

Fitness and glamour magazines can be a blessing or a curse. They are a blessing if they inspire you and give you tips and advice that will help you reach your goals. But they are a curse if they fuel the fires of insecurity as you compare how you look to the models they feature, measure what you should achieve compared to what others have achieved, and feel a sense of uncertainty for not knowing the many things they and their experts tell you. Forget comparing yourself to anyone or anything. Look down your own road and follow your own path to your goals and dreams. Life's too short to get caught up in anything that doesn't help you feel good about yourself.

THIS WEEK'S EXERCISE TIP

A lot of people aren't very flexible and as they get older and perhaps less active, this becomes even more of a problem. Here's an excellent way to limber up without even leaving home. The first stretch will have you sitting on the floor, with your back against the front of the couch or chair. Straighten your legs out in front of you so they are in a V position. Stretch them away from each other as far as you comfortably can and hold it for a few seconds; then bring the legs back in and relax. Bring them back out again just a little farther this time. Hold it there for a few seconds; then bring them back in again and relax. Do this five more times, each time trying to move your legs farther apart. The next stretch will be with your feet on a wall. Simply lie on your back and put your legs up with your heels on the wall in front of you. Allow your legs to spread out in that V shape again and repeat the stretch you did with your legs on the floor. You'll feel even more of a stretch if your body is closer to the wall; likewise, it will be easier the farther your body is away from the wall.

THIS WEEK'S NUTRITION TIP

Here are a few nutrition tidbits from the show called *Did You Know?*

- Diet soda while low in calories is high in phosphoric acid and may deplete and reduce calcium absorption by the body.
- Vitamin B complex (made up of the many vitamins in the B family) can help prevent fatigue, headache, anxiety, insomnia, loss of memory, and irritability.
- Lecithin helps emulsify cholesterol and remove it from blood vessel walls along with helping digestion and keeping nerves healthy.
- Garlic may reduce high blood pressure and lower cholesterol, raising HDL (the good cholesterol) and lowering LDL (the bad cholesterol)?
- Chromium works with insulin to help metabolize sugar and may help reduce heart disease. Good sources of chromium are black-strap molasses, whole wheat flour, and brown sugar.

THE LITTLE THINGS I DID THIS WEEK

FOR NUTRITION:

....
....
....
....
....
....
....
....
....

34

FOR EXERCISE:

....
....
....
....
....
....
....
....
....
....

THE LITTLE THINGS I DID THIS WEEK

TO CHANGE MY THINKING:

....
....
....
....
....
....
....
....
....
....
....

TO HELP INSPIRE MYSELF:

34

....
....
....
....
....
....
....
....
....
....

THE LITTLE THINGS I DID THIS WEEK

THE CHANGES I CAN SEE:

....

....

....

....

....

....

....

....

....

34

THE CHANGES I CAN FEEL:

....

....

....

....

....

....

....

....

....

35
WEEK

"There is a time in every man's education when he arrives at the conviction that envy is ignorance, that imitation is suicide, that he must take himself for better or worse as his portion; that though the wide universe is full of good, no kernel of nourishing corn can come to him but through the toil bestowed on that plot of ground which is given him to till. The power which resides in him is new in nature, and none but he knows what that is which he can do, nor does he know until he has tried....Trust thyself: Every heart vibrates to that iron string."

—Ralph Waldo Emerson

THIS WEEK'S MENTAL TIP

I can give you lots of tips and advice about motivation and exercise, things I know can work wonders for you, but until you trust in yourself to go ahead and give what I tell you a try—and more important until you go ahead and do what you know is right for you—then nothing is going to happen to your body or life except the same old thing. For thousands of years, the wisest people have counseled to "trust thyself." Don't look to others to give you their approval for anything you want to do with your life. If you want to be thinner, then go ahead, eat better and do more exercise. If you want to change jobs or go back to school, then do it. Once you finally let go of the need to please others before you please yourself, then you are on the road to freedom and of finally trusting the most important person you will ever know . . . you!

THIS WEEK'S EXERCISE TIP

One of the easiest, quickest, and simplest things you can do any-where at anytime to change your mood and physiology is deep breathing. Most people are shallow breathers; they only move their body cavity minimally each time they breathe. Yet, when you start deep breathing, good stuff happens inside you. For one, more oxygen intake oxygenates the blood and helps increase blood flow—a good thing. Second, more oxygen to the body and brain awakens the body and immediately changes mood. It's also the technique world-class athletes use to get ready for their performance. Try this: Next time you're feeling tired, listless, or a bit down in the dumps, stand up straight and take ten big breaths in and ten big breaths out and see if that doesn't surprise you.

THIS WEEK'S NUTRITION TIP

Whatever you do in your life, just remember that nothing is important enough to stress over. I know it may be easier for me to say than it is for you to do, but too much stress not only affects you mentally and spiritually but physically and nutritionally as well. Too much stress can cause your body to limit (and in some cases, even stop) making hydrochloric acid, which it needs to digest the foods you eat. And when that happens, proteins aren't used efficiently, which can cause allergies, bloating, and gas. No need to reach for the Tums. Just turn down the mental pressure volume knob inside of you and start enjoying your meals and your life again.

THE LITTLE THINGS I DID THIS WEEK

FOR NUTRITION:

....

....

....

....

....

....

....

....

....

FOR EXERCISE:

....

....

....

....

....

....

....

....

35

THE LITTLE THINGS I DID THIS WEEK

TO CHANGE MY THINKING:

....
....
....
....
....
....
....
....

TO HELP INSPIRE MYSELF:

....
....
....
....
....
....
....

35

THE LITTLE THINGS I DID THIS WEEK

THE CHANGES I CAN SEE:

....

....

....

....

....

....

....

....

....

....

....

....

THE CHANGES I CAN FEEL:

....

....

....

....

....

....

....

....

....

....

35

36
WEEK

"What this power is, I cannot say. All I know is that it exists . . . and it becomes available only when you are in a state of mind in which you know exactly what you want . . . and are fully determined not to quit until you get it."

—ALEXANDER GRAHAM BELL

THIS WEEK'S MENTAL TIP

Are you ready to be amazed? Ready to shake your head at what's about to happen in your life if you'll only do one thing? Then take action. Boldness has power in it and obstacles in your life are demolished when you begin to take action to get what your heart truly desires. The kind of action I'm talking about is the kind that has a passionate desire behind it. And if you're at that point in your life when enough is enough and it's finally time to make some changes in how your body looks and feels, then begin at once to take action and life will guide and inspire you to make it a reality.

THIS WEEK'S EXERCISE TIP

Do I have something to get that butt of yours in shape, and all you have to do is sit on it! Seriously, you can do this at home, work, school, riding in the car, or anywhere you're sitting down or even standing up. I call it the seated glute raise. Go ahead and sit down so you'll know what it's supposed to feel like if you want to do it standing up. While seated, simply squeeze the glute muscles together; as you do, it should raise your upper body off the chair slightly. Hold it there in the elevated position for two to three seconds and then relax. Squeeze the muscle and feel it raise your upper body higher. The key is to really squeeze those glutes together and hold them in that position for a few seconds. Do this a few times throughout the day and do it for a good minute or so each time. No butts about it, you're going to like this little gem.

THIS WEEK'S NUTRITION TIP

Like frozen vegetables? Good, then I've got a great one to keep in your freezer. It's spinach, and it's loaded with lutein that's wonderful for your eyes, bones, brain, and arteries. Not to mention Popeye likes it, too!

THE LITTLE THINGS I DID THIS WEEK

FOR NUTRITION:

FOR EXERCISE:

36

THE LITTLE THINGS I DID THIS WEEK

TO CHANGE MY THINKING:

....

....

....

....

....

....

....

....

....

....

TO HELP INSPIRE MYSELF:

....

....

....

....

....

....

....

....

36

THE LITTLE THINGS I DID THIS WEEK

THE CHANGES I CAN SEE:

THE CHANGES I CAN FEEL:

37
WEEK

"It is never too late to be what you might have been."

—GEORGE ELIOT

THIS WEEK'S MENTAL TIP

Are you twenty years old and unsure what to do with your life? Fantastic! You say you're thirty or forty and would like to make some changes in your life? Perfect! What, you're telling me you've hit the magic fifty-year mark or raced to sixty before you even realized it? Relax, the rest of your life hasn't even begun! No matter how young or old you think or know you are, you are never too young or too old to make changes in your body and life.

THIS WEEK'S EXERCISE TIP

One exercise that you did in school and that the military still does today is push-ups. Depending on how you do them, push-ups will work the arms, chest, and shoulders. And lucky for you, there are easy and difficult ways to do them. First, the easy way. Kneel down. While keeping your knees on the floor, let your upper torso come forward and spread your hands out to about shoulder-width. Push your body up until your arms are locked out. Lower your body and repeat. A more difficult way is to keep your legs locked out and your upper and lower body in a straight line by keeping your knees off the floor and only your feet and hands touching the floor. Push your body up until your arms are locked out. Lower your body and repeat. The third and toughest way to do them is by elevating your legs higher than your head. The higher the legs, the more difficult it will be. Try using different hand positions (e.g., wide, close, more forward or backward, etc.).

THIS WEEK'S NUTRITION TIP

Next time you decide to splurge on a dessert and see that blueberry pie, go for it. Not only does it taste great, it also has lots of those good things for the body called antioxidants that help the brain and body coordination.

THE LITTLE THINGS I DID THIS WEEK

FOR NUTRITION:

....
....
....
....
....
....
....
....
....

FOR EXERCISE:

....
....
....
....
....
....
....
....

37

THE LITTLE THINGS I DID THIS WEEK

TO CHANGE MY THINKING:

....
....
....
....
....
....
....
....
....
....

TO HELP INSPIRE MYSELF:

....
....
....
....
....
....
....
....
....

37

THE LITTLE THINGS I DID THIS WEEK

THE CHANGES I CAN SEE:

....

....

....

....

....

....

....

....

....

....

....

THE CHANGES I CAN FEEL:

....

....

....

....

....

....

....

....

....

....

37

38
WEEK

"If you deliberately plan to be less than you are capable of being, then I warn you, that you will be unhappy for the rest of your life. You will be evading your own capacities and possibilities."

—Dr. Abraham Maslow

THIS WEEK'S MENTAL TIP

Have you ever given anything less than your best effort? Did it feel like you cheated yourself? When we know we are capable of giving more or being better at what we can do, then anything less than our personal best somehow sticks in our minds as less than memorable. Yet there's a fine line you would be wise to walk between doing too much and not doing enough. Take exercise. You can do too much and overtrain or do too little and undertrain; both will hold you back. The secret, if there is one, is to know what your body needs and then do it with your best efforts at that moment on that day. The reward will be more confidence and that can spread to all other areas of your life.

THIS WEEK'S EXERCISE TIP

We all have to go grocery shopping, right? Ah, but what if you could make a little workout out of grocery shopping? Whether you're buying a tub of laundry detergent, milk, or anything that has a bit of weight to it, go ahead and pick it up and hold it longer than you normally would. Lift it a few times up and down and out to your sides to work those shoulders. Or, flex those arms as you curl whatever you're holding up and down. Perhaps as you hold it, quickly bend up and down a few times to work those thighs. The trick is to become more active by doing little bits of exercise here and there in the course of a day while doing the things you'd normally do anyway.

THIS WEEK'S NUTRITION TIP

I've got a fruit for you that will keep your body healthy and . . . shall we say "regular" each day. Prunes. This little fruit is jammin' with all those great antioxidants that a body needs. Try the regular and dried varieties.

THE LITTLE THINGS I DID THIS WEEK

FOR NUTRITION:

FOR EXERCISE:

THE LITTLE THINGS I DID THIS WEEK

TO CHANGE MY THINKING:

....
....
....
....
....
....
....
....
....
....
....

TO HELP INSPIRE MYSELF:

....
....
....
....
....
....
....
....
....
....

38

THE LITTLE THINGS I DID THIS WEEK

THE CHANGES I CAN SEE:

THE CHANGES I CAN FEEL:

38

39
WEEK

"The three big lies: What I don't have is better than what I've got, more is always better and I'll be happy when I finally get what I want."

—Anonymous

THIS WEEK'S MENTAL TIP

The three big translations for that quote:

- The grass is rarely greener on the other side.
- The more things you have, the more they could own you and your life.
- You'll be happy when you give up the need to be happy.

THIS WEEK'S EXERCISE TIP

If you take a shower each day, then it's time we put a little zest in your body. Think of it, doing a cool little workout to get that lower back and those abs in better shape, all while you are having a nice warm shower to relax and soothe the rest of your body. Start with the lower back. Simply turn away from the shower head, put a slight bend to the knees (the legs don't need to be completely locked out), bend over with your upper body, and let your fingers touch the tub underneath you. Bring the upper body up until it's straight up and down and repeat until you've done it fifteen to twenty times. To work those abs, turn around and face the shower head. Keep your body erect with feet standing firmly. Raise your arms and hold them close to your body and in front of you. Now start twisting from side-to-side and do this for one to two minutes without stopping. Start off slowly and you'll find you'll be able to increase your range of motion and your side-to-side speed in no time.

THIS WEEK'S NUTRITION TIP

Be careful of the vitamin robbers. While scientists and research tell us that drinking (wine in particular) in moderation has beneficial health effects, alcohol can also rob the body of B vitamins and, experts say, smoking can rob the body of vitamin C.

THE LITTLE THINGS I DID THIS WEEK

FOR NUTRITION:

FOR EXERCISE:

THE LITTLE THINGS I DID THIS WEEK

TO CHANGE MY THINKING:

....

....

....

....

....

....

....

....

....

....

TO HELP INSPIRE MYSELF:

....

....

....

....

....

....

....

....

39

THE LITTLE THINGS I DID THIS WEEK

THE CHANGES I CAN SEE:

THE CHANGES I CAN FEEL:

WEEK

"You were born an original. Don't die a copy."

—A<small>NONYMOUS</small>

THIS WEEK'S MENTAL TIP

Stop for a moment and be thankful for just one thing: being who and what you are right now. I couldn't care less about the terrific person you're going to be once you do this or achieve that. It doesn't matter to me what you look like, how young or old, wise or unwise you think you are. All that matters is who you are, right now, the person who is reading this. Your life and appearance can change quickly and easily, so that's no big deal. Who I'm admiring and who I want you to admire, perhaps for the first time in a long time, as you look into your mirror before you go to bed tonight, is the one-of-a-kind original masterpiece that's you. Who you are, who you will become, and your life is your gift. How you use it, for the short time you have on this earth, is your gift to yourself and to others. Never sacrifice your gift for anything or anyone.

THIS WEEK'S EXERCISE TIP

We talked about shower exercises last week and now it's time for a bath. These two bathtub exercises will work the abs and stretch out that stiff lower back from a hard day's work. First, the abs. Lie down in the tub as you normally would. Now bend the knees and bring them back toward your waist as you bring the legs and feet up. The feet can even touch the wall or tub wall in front of you if you'd like some support. This is almost the same position you'd be in if you were doing a crunch. Now bring the upper torso up and forward toward the knees and hold it there for one to two seconds and then bring it back down and repeat. Do this twelve to twenty-five times. When you're finished, keep those legs up where they are and this time, with both hands, grab your knees or ankles, and pull them back toward your upper body. Feel it stretch your lower back. Bring the legs back far enough until you can feel a nice stretch in that lower back area and hold it in that position for four to six seconds and then release. Remember, we want no pain, but a stretch that feels oh-so-good to that lower back. Do it three more times just like that.

THIS WEEK'S NUTRITION TIP

People spend billions of dollars each year on skin products, but they've got it wrong. Instead of spending so much money and time taking care of the outside, they'd be surprised how much money they'd save if they took care of the inside first. And when it comes to your skin, that means eating a healthy balanced diet of fresh and nutritious foods and drinking lots of water to hydrate those cells. It also means getting enough vitamin A to keep skin smooth, enough vitamin B to keep skin looking young and firm, and enough vitamin C to keep it pliable, elastic, and resistant to infection.

THE LITTLE THINGS I DID THIS WEEK

FOR NUTRITION:

FOR EXERCISE:

THE LITTLE THINGS I DID THIS WEEK

TO CHANGE MY THINKING:

....
....
....
....
....
....
....
....
....
....

TO HELP INSPIRE MYSELF:

....
....
....
....
....
....
....
....
....

THE LITTLE THINGS I DID THIS WEEK

THE CHANGES I CAN SEE:

THE CHANGES I CAN FEEL:

41
WEEK

"There are two things to aim at in life: first, to get what you want; and, after that, to enjoy it. Only the wisest of mankind achieve the second."

—LOGAN PEARSALL SMITH

THIS WEEK'S MENTAL TIP

Here's what I want you to do at the end of this week and every week you read this book. Take five minutes to recall the little things you did during that week to build a new body and a new you. If you did that one extra rep on a tough exercise, give yourself a pat on the back. If you ate only two scoops of ice cream instead of the usual three, then smile. If you parked farther away from the mall, school, or work just so you could walk for a bit more exercise, then let yourself feel good for a job well done. You see, all those little things are the very things that will make a big difference. By themselves, they may not seem like much, but when you multiply them together, along with all the other little things you did that week, then very quickly and with very little effort you set in motion powerful forces that change bodies and lives in big ways. Each and every week, take a few minutes to enjoy where you are and how far you've come and get excited about next week and all the great things that will happen in your life.

THIS WEEK'S EXERCISE TIP

One of the toughest things you'll have to do is pull yourself back from working out, especially when you're making such great progress, but it's essential that you do. Many people keep exercising, day in and day out, year after year with little to show for their efforts except, perhaps, a body that looks the same, is fast approaching burnout (especially if they've done lots of high-intensity training with inadequate rest and recuperation), and is in a rut. Far too many people find out when it is too late that if they had treated their bodies better and given themselves the rest they needed, they could have avoided being injured and maintained their motivation. These mandatory rest breaks will help you stay injury-free and avoid the pitfalls and frustration of burnout and little or no progress. Keep your body refreshed and renewed, and you will be ready, willing, and able for your next workout schedule. When should you take some time off? I recommend taking at least one full week off from training every four to six weeks. That means, every month and a half, you're going to take a break and do nothing but give your body rest. Go on "workout vacation," relax, do nothing but enjoy yourself. You're going to find that by taking a full week off every four to six weeks, your body will be in a state of progressive results. Meaning, week after week, your body will be improving during that four- to six-week cycle of training. Taking a week off while your body is still in that progressive results cycle will put you in control. You will be the one who has allowed it to stop at that higher level and it will be there that it will start once you come back for your next four- to six-week cycle of training. Think of it as if your body were on a continuous road upward. Each one-week period you take off, your body stops at a rest stop on the way; when you return after that week off to train again, your body gets back on the road upward to the next rest stop.

THIS WEEK'S NUTRITION TIP

I've found a delicious and nonfat ice cream treat you can quickly make yourself. Take a sliver of your favorite nonfat frozen yogurt or ice cream. Spread it on two of your favorite flavored rice cakes (such as blueberry or chocolate or any other flavor) and make a sandwich. Place it in the freezer for at least thirty minutes and eat. Yum...great taste and no fat!

THE LITTLE THINGS I DID THIS WEEK

41

FOR NUTRITION:

....

....

....

....

....

....

....

....

....

....

FOR EXERCISE:

....

....

....

....

....

....

....

....

....

....

THE LITTLE THINGS I DID THIS WEEK

TO CHANGE MY THINKING:

....
....
....
....
....
....
....
....

TO HELP INSPIRE MYSELF:

....
....
....
....
....
....
....

41

THE LITTLE THINGS I DID THIS WEEK

THE CHANGES I CAN SEE:

....

....

....

....

....

....

....

....

....

....

THE CHANGES I CAN FEEL:

....

....

....

....

....

....

....

....

....

41

42
WEEK

"We do not stop playing because we grow old; we grow old because we stop playing."

—Anonymous

THIS WEEK'S MENTAL TIP

I want you to quit working out . . . if it ever becomes unenjoyable. Listen, exercising should be fun and enjoyable if you expect to make it a part of your life. And if it hasn't been in the past, it's time to change that right now. The first thing to know is that you actually need very little time to exercise to get really good results. You only need a few minutes in some cases, so throw away the belief that you must do lengthy workouts or lots of sets and exercises. Next, it's no big deal if you miss a workout here and there or if your diet goes to heck in a handbasket. Just start back where you left off and you'll be fine. You see, working out and all the other things in your life are much more meaningful when they're fun and when you can look forward to doing them; that's when your life gets back to making you happy. As they say, life is much too important to be taken seriously.

THIS WEEK'S EXERCISE TIP

One of the best exercises I've found for the legs is one you can do at home and all you need is your body and a wall. They're called Wall Deep Knee Bends and they work great. Think of doing these just like a squat, only with no weight. In essence, all you're really doing is keeping your upper body erect and bending at the knees and squatting up and down. Where you place your feet will affect, to some degree, where you feel the exercise. Legs close and feet pointed straight ahead and you'll most likely feel it in the overall quad and this should help give your legs a nice outer sweep. Feet turned out and away from the body will tend to place the emphasis on the inner thighs. Legs and feet turned farther out and away from the body—like a ballet-type stance—shifts more work on the inner and upper/inner thigh. Regardless of legs and feet position, always make sure the knees travel in a straight line over the toes. To really make the quads burn, try doing these deep knee bends with your back against a wall. This will add resistance to the exercise and definitely make the legs work harder while helping you maintain strict form. Try to go down to the parallel position and do nonstop reps for even better results.

THIS WEEK'S NUTRITION TIP

Let me give you a little tip to remember that has worked well for lots of people: Too many carbs will make you drowsy and too much protein will keep you awake. Now, use that tip if you're planning for a big meeting and you need to be mentally sharp by eating some extra protein like lowfat or nonfat yogurt, cottage cheese, skim milk, or a half sandwich of turkey breast on whole wheat. Likewise, if you've had a million things on your mind and you're pretty amped up and want to power down, try eating some extra carbs like a small plate of pasta and a scoop or two of lowfat or nonfat frozen yogurt or ice cream.

THE LITTLE THINGS I DID THIS WEEK

42

FOR NUTRITION:

....

....

....

....

....

....

....

....

....

FOR EXERCISE:

....

....

....

....

....

....

....

....

THE LITTLE THINGS I DID THIS WEEK

TO CHANGE MY THINKING:

....
....
....
....
....
....
....
....
....

TO HELP INSPIRE MYSELF:

....
....
....
....
....
....
....
....
....

THE LITTLE THINGS I DID THIS WEEK

THE CHANGES I CAN SEE:

....

....

....

....

....

....

....

....

....

....

THE CHANGES I CAN FEEL:

....

....

....

....

....

....

....

....

....

WEEK

"*Never build a case against yourself.*"

—ROBERT ROWBOTTOM

THIS WEEK'S MENTAL TIP

Whenever you think about trying something new, is it easier for you to give more reasons why you can do it or why you cannot? If you hesitated and wanted to say you could think of more reasons why you could do it; but knew it wasn't true, then welcome to a big club. Forget having enemies, people simply don't need them when they've got the toughest foe they'll ever face staring right at them—themselves! Next time when you're out in public, listen to what people say to each other. You'll be amazed to hear just how negative, self-defeating, and deflating are the things people tell each other about themselves. Truly, if you say over and over again what your limitations are, don't be surprised at just how quickly they come true.

THIS WEEK'S EXERCISE TIP

You probably wouldn't think so, but simply moving the elbows up or down, or into the body or away, can affect how an exercise feels. Remember the dumbbell kickback for the triceps. Most people will do this exercise with their working upper arm either close to their body or down below their body. Wrong! The trick is to keep the upper arm close to the body but make it come up above the upper body. Do a dumbbell triceps kickback and the higher you raise the working elbow and dumbbell above your body, the tougher this exercise will get. Now, try changing arm, elbow, and foot positions on other exercises and see if you can feel the difference.

THIS WEEK'S NUTRITION TIP

Time to get rid of that nasty LDL (low-density lipoprotein) cholesterol with some great foods that you probably have in the pantry or refrigerator: oat bran, oatmeal, barley, grapefruit, skim milk, garlic, onions, eggplant, olive oil, apples, oranges, carrots, and yogurt.

THE LITTLE THINGS I DID THIS WEEK

FOR NUTRITION:

....

....

....

....

....

....

....

....

....

FOR EXERCISE:

....

....

....

....

....

....

....

43

THE LITTLE THINGS I DID THIS WEEK

TO CHANGE MY THINKING:

TO HELP INSPIRE MYSELF:

THE LITTLE THINGS I DID THIS WEEK

THE CHANGES I CAN SEE:

....

....

....

....

....

....

....

....

....

THE CHANGES I CAN FEEL:

....

....

....

....

....

....

....

....

WEEK 44

"When you get into a tight place and everything goes against you, till it seems as though you could not hold on a minute longer, never give up then, for that is just the place and time that the tide will turn."

—HARRIET BEECHER STOWE

THIS WEEK'S MENTAL TIP

One thing about life that'll amaze you is how much things and lives can change in twenty-four hours. One day, it could be the last straw in a series of events you think you can no longer take and then the next day, the good news comes in and changes everything in a flash. The same is true of exercise and diet. It may seem like weeks will go by as you have put time and work into doing all the right things, and yet, little, if any, progress comes your way. Then a few days later, your eyes open to the new changes you begin to see taking place in your body. Those few extra pounds that just wouldn't come off are finally disappearing. And it's all because you hung in there when you felt like giving up.

THIS WEEK'S EXERCISE TIP

Some weeks back, I talked to you about push-ups and what a terrific exercise they are. Well, here's another way to do them that will work chest and triceps, and it's standing up and against a wall. Keeping your body erect, stand about twelve to twenty-four inches away from a wall. Place your hands on the wall—hands spaced wide works more of the chest and hands; closer works more triceps. Let your body come forward toward the wall and then push it back out to the starting position and repeat. Don't allow your body to bend as it comes forward; keep it straight.

THIS WEEK'S NUTRITION TIP

Now let's raise that good HDL (high-density lipoprotein) cholesterol with such things as raw onions, olive oil, wine (go for the red variety), beer, and spirits (experts say one to two drinks a day is okay). Of course, keeping your diet low-fat will really help.

THE LITTLE THINGS I DID THIS WEEK

FOR NUTRITION:

....

....

....

....

....

....

....

....

FOR EXERCISE:

....

....

....

....

....

....

....

44

THE LITTLE THINGS I DID THIS WEEK

TO CHANGE MY THINKING:

....

....

....

....

....

....

....

....

....

TO HELP INSPIRE MYSELF:

....

....

....

....

....

....

....

44

THE LITTLE THINGS I DID THIS WEEK

THE CHANGES I CAN SEE:

THE CHANGES I CAN FEEL:

44

WEEK 45

"Sometimes it is more important to discover what one cannot do than what one can do. So much restlessness is due to the fact that a man does not know what he wants, or he wants too many things, or perhaps he wants to be somebody else, to be anybody except himself."

—LIN YUTANG

THIS WEEK'S MENTAL TIP

I've heard it said that in our lives we can have *anything*, it's just that we can't have *everything*. There's a big difference. We simply aren't given enough years to have everything there is to have. But, for the things we deeply desire, we can most definitely have them if we'll do what is required to make them our own. Each person has talents and abilities that allow him or her to do things more easily than someone else. Each person has callings in life and the wisest are those who listen to that calling and follow it. The problem, it seems, comes when we don't know what we want or we think we'll have forever to do whatever it is we finally decide to do. The truth is we don't have unlimited time to fulfill our unlimited desires. We are all given the same 1,440 minutes each day, and each person has a certain number of years to make the most of each of those days. Each day you choose not to follow your dreams is one less day you'll have to enjoy it when you do. When we think we can be all things to all people and neglect our limitations, no matter how big or small they may be, we waste time and become frustrated and disappointed. Follow the voice of your calling today.

THIS WEEK'S EXERCISE TIP

The old proverb that says "The person who does not find time for exercise will have to find time for illness" speaks volumes about how important exercise is to your life. From the ancient Greeks to Thomas Jefferson, a simple walk (one that doesn't fatigue you) has been touted as the best single exercise a person could do; even today, few would argue. The Greeks also believed that life was movement and the more movement they did, the more the life force would course through their body and the better they would feel and the longer they would live. So, don't sweat it if you have no time for a gym, no time for a proper workout with machines, weights, and the like. Simply walk more.

THIS WEEK'S NUTRITION TIP

We all like junk food every now and then. The practice of eating a good diet for six days and then on the seventh day relaxing and having those junk foods you've been craving works great for lots of people. And to really give your body the disease-fighting and life-sustaining nutrients it needs (the phytochemicals), try eating more foods that have been shown to help the body prevent disease such as peppers, red beets, citrus fruit, onions, garlic, bok choy, Brussels sprouts, grapes, broccoli, cabbage, mustard greens, cauliflower, leeks, carrots, apples, rutabagas, chives, collards, turnip greens, kale, kohlrabi, and tomatoes.

THE LITTLE THINGS I DID THIS WEEK

FOR NUTRITION:

....

....

....

....

....

....

....

....

....

45

....

....

FOR EXERCISE:

....

....

....

....

....

....

....

....

....

....

THE LITTLE THINGS I DID THIS WEEK

TO CHANGE MY THINKING:

....

....

....

....

....

....

....

....

....

TO HELP INSPIRE MYSELF:

....

....

....

....

....

....

....

....

45

THE LITTLE THINGS I DID THIS WEEK

THE CHANGES I CAN SEE:

THE CHANGES I CAN FEEL:

46
WEEK

"All through history we find convincing proof that mental powers increase with age, that artistic and intellectual powers are often intensified in later years. Michelangelo was still producing masterpieces at eighty-nine. Goethe completed the second part of Faust when he was eighty-two. Wagner finished Parsifal *at sixty-nine, and* Voltaire wrote Candide *at sixty-five. Handel was still composing beautiful music, Longfellow was still writing immortal poetry, after seventy."*

—LILLIAN EICHLER WATSON

THIS WEEK'S MENTAL TIP

"The older you get, the wiser you become" is a maxim that's just as true today as it was hundreds of years ago. And with that wisdom comes the realization that age matters not when you decide to become masterful at almost anything in life. The point is to decide to be great at something. Many times we think it advantageous that others started their quest to greatness at such an early age, only later to find out that those we admired are miserable because they gave up so many precious years of their youth in order to become so great. And, for many of them, if they had it to do all over again, they would've waited and experienced more of life and allowed their genius to unfold and develop without such all-or-nothing drive and determination to be first while still young. Whatever your age and whatever your experience, right now is the best time to begin your quest for greatness, be it a refreshed body, heart, and soul, or a new direction in your life.

THIS WEEK'S EXERCISE TIP

Hey, here's a stealthy little exercise that works your abs that no one will know you are doing. Stand or sit. With your upper body erect, breathe out; then take a deep breath in—as big a breath in as possible—and hold it for three to five seconds. Blow that big (not bad) breath out and do it again. Do this twelve to fifteen times two or three times a day for a cool little stomach toner.

THIS WEEK'S NUTRITION TIP

One of the cheapest, easiest, and tastiest ways to help keep your body feeling good and your colon healthy and disease-free is by eating wheat bran each day. And all you need is just one cup of your favorite wheat bran cereal to do it.

THE LITTLE THINGS I DID THIS WEEK

FOR NUTRITION:

....

....

....

....

....

....

....

....

FOR EXERCISE:

....

....

....

....

....

....

....

46

THE LITTLE THINGS I DID THIS WEEK

TO CHANGE MY THINKING:

....

....

....

....

....

....

....

....

....

....

46

TO HELP INSPIRE MYSELF:

....

....

....

....

....

....

....

....

....

....

THE LITTLE THINGS I DID THIS WEEK

THE CHANGES I CAN SEE:

....
....
....
....
....
....
....
....

THE CHANGES I CAN FEEL:

....
....
....
....
....
....
....
....

WEEK 47

"When it comes to your life, bet everything you have and bet it all on yourself."

—ROBERT WOLFF

THIS WEEK'S MENTAL TIP

The body and life you've been given is not an eternal challenge to be forever unhappy and always wanting to change. You can have no desire to change how you look and feel and be as happy as those who do. It's all about what you desire to make different in your life and why. Have you allowed yourself to be sucked into the competitive vibe and let that be your guide to what you should do next? Or, have you unlocked those chains and decided to live your life and look and feel the way you do because that's exactly what you want without a care as to what others think? If so, then congratulations for being on the road to living happily, and well. You don't need to prove anything to anyone else. With or without change, with or without success, you are just as awesome and you don't need anyone to tell you otherwise.

THIS WEEK'S EXERCISE TIP

Here's a wonderful series of quick and easy exercises you can do any-where or anytime to help keep you flexible, increase your range of motion, and lower your stress level. The first is for the wrists. Hold the right wrist with the left hand and freely move the right hand in a big cir-cle from left to right, right to left. Repeat for the other hand. Now do the same kind of movement for the ankles. You can either sit down and hold the one ankle with the other hand and do it or while standing, lift the leg off the ground and move the foot in a circle from right to left and left to right. And now for a great de-stressor for the head and neck. Slowly begin turning your head from left to right. Do this eight to ten times. Next, allow the head to relax and let it hang down as you turn it slowly and gently from side to side. Finally, while relaxed, begin turning your head in a relaxing circle and do this for six times to the right, and then six times to the left. Relax and feel the stress and tension evaporate from your body each time your head moves.

THIS WEEK'S NUTRITION TIP

Things are going to get a little fishy here. Time for some fish tips.

- Try having fish one to three times a week.
- Go for the smaller fish since they have fewer years and chances of being exposed to chemicals and pollutants than their older brothers and sisters.
- Freshwater salmon or trout is good, but you might want to lean more on saltwater fish than other freshwater fish.
- Try this recipe for cooking fish—either on the grill or in the oven: Place the fish in aluminum foil, baste with a light coat of extra virgin olive oil. Sprinkle basil or rosemary leaves over it; add a good squeeze of lemon juice. Cover completely and cook at 300 to 350 degrees for twenty minutes. Unwrap, serve, and simply throw away the wrapper. No mess or smell, and it's almost effortless.

THE LITTLE THINGS I DID THIS WEEK

FOR NUTRITION:

FOR EXERCISE:

47

THE LITTLE THINGS I DID THIS WEEK

TO CHANGE MY THINKING:

....

....

....

....

....

....

....

....

....

....

....

....

47

TO HELP INSPIRE MYSELF:

....

....

....

....

....

....

....

....

....

....

THE LITTLE THINGS I DID THIS WEEK

THE CHANGES I CAN SEE:

THE CHANGES I CAN FEEL:

47

255

48

WEEK

"If a man does not keep pace with his compan-
ions, perhaps it is because he hears a different
drummer. Let him keep step to the music which
he hears, however measured or far away."

—HENRY DAVID THOREAU

THIS WEEK'S MENTAL TIP

You may begin an exercise program or different diet and it could be the very one that's the latest buzz or bestseller everyone is following, and yet it doesn't do anything for you. And not following it any longer is the very best thing you can do. Regardless of your experience, you have an unfailing inner knowing that understands what works and what doesn't in your life. Follow wherever it leads you. You're much smarter and wiser than you may think.

THIS WEEK'S EXERCISE TIP

You've been doing great all these weeks trying lots of the different exercises and tips I've been giving you. It's time for a sleep tip. After all, sleep is just as important to the body as exercise, if not more so. This one's easy: Get rid of the alarm clock and notice how much better you sleep. Trust your own body clock to wake you, and you'll be amazed at how much more restfully you'll sleep and how much better you'll feel when you wake up.

THIS WEEK'S NUTRITION TIP

For all of us wanting our bodies to be lean machines, a good rule of thumb to follow is that as the day gets later, reduce the amount of carbohydrates while keeping the protein intake consistent. Many believe that one reason to do this is that the body's insulin is more active earlier in the day than in the evening. And if the body's ability to use and move insulin is lower at night, it suggests a greater likelihood that those great-tasting carbohydrate late-night snacks could be more easily stored as fat.

THE LITTLE THINGS I DID THIS WEEK

FOR NUTRITION:

....

....

....

....

....

....

....

....

....

....

FOR EXERCISE:

....

....

....

....

....

....

....

....

....

....

48

THE LITTLE THINGS I DID THIS WEEK

TO CHANGE MY THINKING:

....
....
....
....
....
....
....
....
....
....
....

TO HELP INSPIRE MYSELF:

....
....
....
....
....
....
....
....
....
....

48

THE LITTLE THINGS I DID THIS WEEK

THE CHANGES I CAN SEE:

....

....

....

....

....

....

....

....

....

....

....

THE CHANGES I CAN FEEL:

....

....

....

....

....

....

....

....

....

48

WEEK 49

"*Before we set our hearts too much upon any-thing, let us examine how happy they are who already possess it.*"

—FRANÇOIS DE LA ROCHEFOUCAULD

THIS WEEK'S MENTAL TIP

Oh, my goodness, how we think we'd be so much happier if we only could have more time, money, success, or anything else we don't have in our lives right now. Speaking from experience, I can tell you that I've known many women and men who had all the beauty you could ask for and all the problems you'd never want. While much of their lives was focused on the physical, far less of it was devoted to the mental and spiritual. Once you got beyond the outer shell, you could immediately sense the void inside. Sure, you'd like to change a few things in your life, try something new, get rid of things that aren't working any longer, and I know you'll do it. But on the way to doing those things, let yourself be happy for who you are right now. Perhaps it isn't so bad after all?

THIS WEEK'S EXERCISE TIP

So, how do you know when you're making progress? The first way is to ask yourself, how do you feel? If you're feeling better about yourself and your body, then you're doing something right and making progress. The next step is to accurately assess how you look. And don't use the scale to do it. If you put too much emphasis on achieving a certain number—as in losing or gaining weight (remember the majority of scales tell you how much weight, not fat, you've lost)—then much of how you feel about yourself and your progress will be tied to what the scale tells you. And the scale doesn't tell you the changing composition of your body. As you know, muscle weighs more than fat and if your body is changing and losing fat and adding a bit of lean, healthy muscle tissue, you can actually look and feel better and weigh more! If you are just paying attention to how much you weigh, then the added weight may steal your motivation; you will lose your inspiration to keep working out. To really get a good indication of how your body is changing (and it will, believe me), use a mirror. The mirror doesn't care about how much you weigh. It simply reflects back to you what you look like at that given moment of the day. And your body can change greatly from hour to hour and day to day as a result of hormones, sleep, food and fluid intake, water retention, and so on. So if you must look in the mirror, then try doing it at different times on different days to see how your body changes. The other feedback method is to use a pair of old tight-fitting pants. If you're still having problems getting them on, then you've got a bit more work to do. If the pants are getting easier to slip on or getting loose, then you're on the right track. Be careful of using just any kind of pants, especially jeans that have just been washed and dried; they can shrink up and make you think you're heavier than you really are.

THIS WEEK'S NUTRITION TIP

If you have trouble falling asleep every now and then, try eating a light snack about forty-five to sixty minutes before bedtime that has sugar or honey on it. Stay away from the high-fat cookies and snacks. Instead, try eating a bagel or rice cake with a nice spread of honey and see if that doesn't do the trick.

THE LITTLE THINGS I DID THIS WEEK

FOR NUTRITION:

FOR EXERCISE:

49

THE LITTLE THINGS I DID THIS WEEK

TO CHANGE MY THINKING:

TO HELP INSPIRE MYSELF:

THE LITTLE THINGS I DID THIS WEEK

THE CHANGES I CAN SEE:

....

....

....

....

....

....

....

....

....

....

....

....

THE CHANGES I CAN FEEL:

....

....

....

....

....

....

....

....

....

49

50
WEEK

"All that is necessary to break the spell of inertia and frustration is this: Act as if it were impossible to fail. This is the talisman, the formula, the command of right-about-face which turns us from failure towards success."

—DOROTHEA BRANDE

THIS WEEK'S MENTAL TIP

This quote has been a source of power and inspiration so many times in my life. Think of it: Act as if it were impossible to fail! Just what would you attempt if you knew you couldn't fail? Just what kinds of changes would you make in mind, body, and spirit if you knew success was guaranteed? William James, the Harvard scholar and philosopher, paraphrased all of this beautifully when he said, "Act as if, and you will soon become." See yourself and act as if you are the greatest success and it is impossible for you to fail.

THIS WEEK'S EXERCISE TIP

I like this exercise for strengthening and toning the lower back because it's quick, easy, and you can do it at home. Lie down with your stomach touching the floor. Keep your legs and feet close together. Place your arms and hands under your upper legs, with your hands turned so that your palms are touching the floor. Slowly raise your upper body a few inches off the floor until you can feel your lower back working. Hold your body in this a-few-inches-off-the-floor position for one to two seconds and then slowly lower it back down and repeat. Be sure to do slow continuous-tension reps and you won't need to do more than five to nine per set and only two to three sets.

THIS WEEK'S NUTRITION TIP

Here are a few cooking and food storage tips to make your life easier. One: keep your cereal in the refrigerator; it'll last longer. Two: when broiling food, add one-half to one cup of water before cooking; the water keeps the smoke away and sops up the grease. Three: to keep that pot of spaghetti, rice, or noodles from boiling over, add a tablespoon of cooking oil to it. Four: to keep cheese from getting all funky and moldy, next time try storing it in a glass jar.

THE LITTLE THINGS I DID THIS WEEK

FOR NUTRITION:

FOR EXERCISE:

50

THE LITTLE THINGS I DID THIS WEEK

TO CHANGE MY THINKING:

....

....

....

....

....

....

....

....

....

....

....

....

TO HELP INSPIRE MYSELF:

....

....

....

....

....

....

....

....

....

....

50

THE LITTLE THINGS I DID THIS WEEK

THE CHANGES I CAN SEE:

....

....

....

....

....

....

....

....

....

....

THE CHANGES I CAN FEEL:

....

....

....

....

....

....

....

....

....

50

51
WEEK

"Nobody grows old by merely living a number of years; people grow old only by deserting their ideals. Years wrinkle the skin, but to give up enthusiasm wrinkles the soul . . . Whether seventy or sixteen, there is in every being's heart the love of wonder, the sweet amazement at the stars and the starlike things and thoughts, the undaunted challenge of events, the unfailing childlike appetite for what's next, and the joy and the game of life. You are as young as your faith, as old as your doubt; as young as your self-confidence, as old as your fear; as young as your hope, as old as your despair."

—SAMUEL ULLMAN

THIS WEEK'S MENTAL TIP

To be young, you must do three things. Number one: Think young; old thoughts make old people. Number two: Be active. Number three: Live your life and forget your age.

THIS WEEK'S EXERCISE TIP

Knowing how to exercise makes it fun. Knowing how to avoid injuries makes it something you'll enjoy doing for the rest of your life. Here are the rules to remember:

Rule #1: Make time to warm up before, during, and after training.

Rule #2: Go slowly and steadily. Be sure to use good exercise form and be consistent.

Rule #3: If at any time you feel something that is painful (you'll be able to differentiate between good old-fashioned making-the-muscles-work discomfort, which is normal, and real pain), stop immediately and don't do that exercise. Stretch some more and then try another exercise; if the pain persists, cool down and take a break.

Rule #4: Allow your body to rest completely and heal that injury. Even if many days have passed and you can still feel a slight twinge or ache, continue to rest. If you feel the pain, then do not train!

Rule #5: Once you have returned to 100 percent, begin very slowly by moving that body part with no weights. Start with a very limited range of motion and slowly and gradually increase the range of motion until it is pain-free and back to 100 percent normal.

Rule #6: Once it is 100 percent normal and you feel no pain or discomfort, add a very light set of an exercise for that body part that is easy and comfortable for you to do. Focus on doing any kind of exercise that allows for the freest range of movement and one that will allow you to find the right exercise groove that feels best for you and your body.

Rule #7: Next workout, add another weight set of that exercise. Each workout, slowly add another weight exercise until you're back to the level before the injury. Add weight, sets, reps, and exercises slowly and stop immediately if you feel ANY pain.

Rule #8: Add a new segment to your workout that includes more emphasis on stretching, increasing range of motion, and warm-ups for any sensitive body parts or areas you might have.

Rule #9: Take at least one week off from training for every four to six weeks of training you do. Even if you're making great progress, feeling no injuries, no pain, no discomfort, take the time off. Force yourself, if you have to, to take the time off. It will do amazing things for your body, attitude, and results.

THIS WEEK'S NUTRITION TIP

More and more people are looking for foods that have fewer chemicals and processing and are more organic. Besides the taste differences, you might be surprised at the nutritious benefits when comparing organic to nonorganic foods. For example, in one experiment that caught my eye, researchers found organically grown potatoes had at least two times the boron and selenium, and over 50 percent more zinc than nonorganic potatoes. And organically grown wheat was equally impressive: two times more calcium, four times more magnesium, five times more manganese, and thirteen times more selenium than the nonorganic type.

THE LITTLE THINGS I DID THIS WEEK

FOR NUTRITION:

....

....

....

....

....

....

....

....

FOR EXERCISE:

....

....

....

....

....

....

....

....

51

THE LITTLE THINGS I DID THIS WEEK

TO CHANGE MY THINKING:

....

....

....

....

....

....

....

....

....

TO HELP INSPIRE MYSELF:

....

....

....

....

....

....

....

....

....

51

THE LITTLE THINGS I DID THIS WEEK

THE CHANGES I CAN SEE:

THE CHANGES I CAN FEEL:

52
WEEK

"Doubt whom you will, but never yourself."

—CHRISTIAN BOVEE

THIS WEEK'S MENTAL TIP

When you look back on what has happened in your life and the decisions you've made and the things you've gone through as a result of those decisions, you'll start realizing something surprising. Everything that has happened to you, either happy or painful, has made you who and what you are today. And if you go back to an event that may have happened years ago and wonder how your life would've been different if you could erase that experience, you'll see that you wouldn't want to erase it because it was the next step you needed to lead you to the next thing that happened in your life. So many times you beat yourself up for the decisions you did or did not make only to realize that not only did you make the best decision you could've made at that time in your life, years later, you see that going through such an experience turned out to be a huge blessing and a growing experience that you needed. You have never failed and you never will fail because you will make the best decisions you can, at the right times, on that day, and at that time in your life. Yes, the uncertainties of the economy, the events of the world, and the actions of other people may cause you to have doubt, but never doubt yourself, for you will always make the right decisions and you always have.

THIS WEEK'S EXERCISE TIP

Here's when it's good to be in a jamb; a doorjamb, that is. If you're ever short on time but high on enthusiasm to do at least a little something for your body, try these immovable resistance exercises that will work the arms, shoulders, and chest. First, stand in a doorway or hallway. Place both hands on either side of you and against the door jamb or hallway. Begin to push against the walls and push for three to six seconds, then release. Do this again two more times. You'll feel this in the arms, chest, and shoulders. Next, with arms out to your sides, place the back of the hands against the door jamb or hallway and do the same push for three to six seconds like you did before. Do this two more times. This will work the shoulders more directly. Finally, while standing in the middle of the doorway, raise both arms above your head so the hands are touching the top of the doorway. Keep your body erect and now push the arms upward as you try to straighten them; feel it work the shoulders. And as a bonus, if the doorway or hallway is wide enough, you can place your body with your back on one side of the doorway or hallway and one foot on the opposite side. Push your leg and hold it for three to six seconds against the immovable object. Do it for the other leg and you should feel as though you've had a quick little workout.

THIS WEEK'S NUTRITION TIP

This is an easy one: Eat more of the foods that are good for your body, but be sure to eat the foods you enjoy. Your life is not some scientific experiment that's a test for you to cut out the things you enjoy and eat simply for the sake of seeing how long you can live. Who the heck cares how many years you live if you haven't fully enjoyed the years you have lived so far? There'll be days and times when your diet will be terrible and other times when it will be spot on. Just realize that you are here to do the best you can when you can, enjoy each day and the wonderful opportunities of choosing the foods you eat, and most of all, cherish the gift of your life.

"Enjoy yourself—it is later than you think."

—Dr. Frederic Loomis

THE LITTLE THINGS I DID THIS WEEK

FOR NUTRITION:

FOR EXERCISE:

THE LITTLE THINGS I DID THIS WEEK

TO CHANGE MY THINKING:

....

....

....

....

....

....

....

....

....

....

TO HELP INSPIRE MYSELF:

....

....

....

....

....

....

....

....

....

....

52

THE LITTLE THINGS I DID THIS WEEK

THE CHANGES I CAN SEE:

....

....

....

....

....

....

....

....

....

....

THE CHANGES I CAN FEEL:

....

....

....

....

....

....

....

....

....

52